To darling Henry
with all my love
Lorrie

SIGNALS

SIGNALS

A Young Refugee's Flight
from Germany in the Thirties

Frederick G. Cohn

UNITED WRITERS
Cornwall

UNITED WRITERS PUBLICATIONS LTD
Ailsa, Castle Gate, Penzance, Cornwall.

British Library Cataloguing in Publication Data
Cohn, Frederick G.
Signals
1. Germany. Jews. Escapes, 1939-1945
I. Title
940.531503924

ISBN 1 85200 028 7

Printed in Great Britain by
United Writers Publications Ltd
Cornwall

This exploration is dedicated to Hans.

PREFACE

The events described in this autobiographical narrative took place in a dark period of Germany's history. The names of the characters have been changed. It is an attempt to record the experiences and feelings of a young refugee who eventually escaped persecution and annihilation.

He shares with many thousands of people forced to flee their native countries, not only the immediate fear of death and the physical deprivations, but the knowledge that they are outcasts — worthless and rootless.

For such human tragedies we are all responsible.

F. G. C.

'Unless God send his hail
Or blinding fire balls,
    sleet or stifling snow,
In some time, his good time,
I shall arrive.'

Robert Browning: Paracelsus Pt. I

CONTENTS

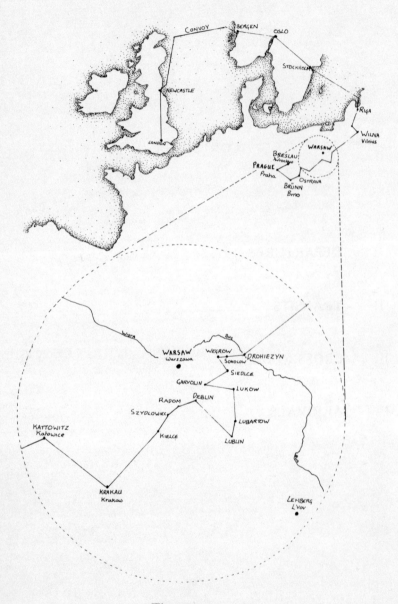

The escape route.

I

DEPARTURES

Many times I have tried to record what happened to Paul and me during the war in Poland. I find fragments of my vain efforts in old folders where I keep letters and other papers. Why was I not able to write about what I have always regarded to be the most important episode in my life?

I lacked the skill in the use of words. And how was I to structure such an account? As soon as I thought of one particular incident, others entered my mind, events of my childhood which apparently had nothing to do with what happened later when I was in my teens.

As soon as I settled down to write, a feeling of emptiness, a kind of paralysis overcame me.

When I put pen to paper or fingers on the keys of the typewriter, I felt physically sick. What had not yet been expressed was already rejected.

But the story has to be told. I am committed to tell it. Time is getting short. I am already in my late sixties.

When I was a boy I was convinced I was born to be a poet. Georg my friend, whom I loved deeply, said:

"Martin, how I envy you. Hang on to this gift of yours. Don't lose it."

Georg died in an extermination camp. My gift died too.

We emigrated from Germany when I was sixteen years old. The next years were not lean ones. They were full of confu-

11

sion: unrealistic hopes, disappointments and terrors.

Later in England it was necessary to learn a new language. I wanted to be assimilated. I wanted to be no different from others. I had to learn how to cope with unfamiliar situations. This took effort. It is not surprising that my small talent for writing had little chance of survival.

To be uprooted means more than leaving one country for another. There is the language. How many of us can find the adopted language as rich in colour and in meaning as the mother tongue? I have forgotten much of my German. But English still feels strange at times, strange and foreign, even now after so many years in Britain. I shall always remain a foreigner.

I am trying to explain. I am trying to explain why I have failed to do what I wanted to do for so many years.

Perhaps if I can talk to you, haltingly, simply, without having to pay regard to the structure of the narrative, the flow of sentences, the use of words and all the other technicalities associated with writing, if you just let me talk, talk in my own way: it may be possible now.

I can talk about myself and my brother, about Martin and Paul Rosen, as if they were fictional characters in a novel, and indeed I can see them both somewhere in an alien landscape, removed from me. It seems incredible that I, Martin, and Paul, my brother, acted in the way we did.

I can talk to you about incidents in my childhood, apparently unrelated to what was to come. (But then I believe what happened to me as a child was a kind of preparation.) I shall try not to bring into my narration – if one can call my disjointed stutter a narration – the experience of a middle-aged man. This is Martin's story, Martin who is nineteen and trying to grow up. Sometimes it may be helpful to look into the future, a future of which Martin was, of course, ignorant.

There are not many who can point to a particular phase in

their lives and say: these weeks were the most significant ones. I am fortunate, I know. I can state without hesitation that the weeks in September and October 1939 have shaped me.

When Paul and I arrived in this country in March the following year, my father asked us to note down what happened during the five weeks in Poland. This belated diary covered the main events on one and a half sheets of paper. Ten years ago Paul made use of this very short diary and retraced with my help our steps once more. This resulted in an extended account. His manuscript lies by me. The sequence of happenings as recorded by Paul is quite correct, indeed it is a clear factual version. Both the short diary and Paul's extended report bear witness to what I am going to tell. They are not only necessary reminders but will help me to distinguish dream from reality.

Nearly fifty-one years have passed since the Second World War started and some experiences seem implausible — yes even to me, to me. These aides-mémoire are for this reason important. Dreams I shall keep to myself. I shall invent nothing.

This will definitely be my last attempt. I shall not try again.

*　　*　　*　　*

It was a dark night. All the lights in the buildings and in the streets had been switched off. The ghostly silhouettes of the houses stretched towards the sky like warning fingers. Martin walked to and fro in front of the house of flats where he and his brother lived. Fire-watching. He had not been told what he was to do in case of fire, but then it was only an exercise. The Germans would certainly not be so stupid as to start a war. The Polish army was well prepared, according to the radio and the newspapers. Some pact with Britain had been made. "Poland is not Czechoslovakia," Uncle Zimmermann had said more than once. But Martin was not so sure. There were so many people parading in front of their black homes, on their own or in twos or threes, talking excitedly, as if they expected something to happen.

13

'If the Germans invade Poland,' Martin thought, 'this will be the end for us. Kattowitz is only a few kilometres from the German border. We could not get away in time . . . At least the parents are safe. But why, why could we not get our permits in time to go with them to England?'

He shook his head.

"There will be no war," he said to himself, "no war. Tomorrow we shall see our names on the list for transport to London."

But he did not really believe it.

There were also rumours around that the frontiers had already been closed. Of course, nobody knew anything for certain.

Martin peered at his watch. It was nearly four, time to go upstairs and wake Paul. It was his turn.

Paul was convinced war was inevitable. He gave good reasons. Nothing could stop the Germans now. The British were only likely to interfere when it was already too late. A week ago some agreement had been reached between Germany and Russia. The situation was without hope. Their own future looked bleak.

"There are a lot of people about," said Martin to Paul who quickly dressed.

"It's a crazy idea to organise an air-raid exercise, now that war is practically upon us," said Paul, "what are we supposed to learn from it? How to expose ourselves to the raining bombs?"

"There are no bombs."

"Not yet, but they will come. No doubt, they will come." And he went downstairs.

*　　*　　*　　*

Martin threw off the blankets from his bed. It was hot. He covered himself with a sheet. The memory of his birthday last week kept him awake.

He thought: 'I am not superstitious, but there are signs. I believe in signs.'

The parents had written, not just the usual birthday letter, but telling the boys that the Home Office had now

14

given them both permits and that they would be included in the next transport to London. 'We shall soon see each other again,' his mother wrote, 'we shall then celebrate your birthday in style. A good omen: I found a four-leaved clover in Richmond Park yesterday. This is your present. I know it will bring luck to you both — to all of us.' Martin touched it. In the afternoon he went with Frau Kranz and her daughter Ursel for a walk. The weather was fine, all three were happy. Paul was elsewhere. Martin was ashamed to admit to himself that he was glad his brother was not with them. His negativism would have spoilt the day. 'Everything is normal,' Martin thought, 'smiling people in their summer clothes, children playing noisily, and Ursel's chatter. A disaster is unthinkable.'

Ursel did not seem to mind Martin's misshapen upper lip, of which Martin was always so conscious, particularly when talking to girls. "What are your plans?" he asked, "I mean, with the Germans on your doorstep, no Jew in Poland is safe."

Ursel replied that neither she nor her mother had given the matter much thought.

"I still have three years at school and then we might go to the United States. We've got some relatives living there."

"If you should pass through England, you must let us know. It would be nice to meet again."

Ursel smiled. "What will you do when you get settled in London?" she asked.

"I don't know. I am not as clever as Paul. I am not much good at studying. I'm not practically minded either. I'll do something, I expect."

Frau Kranz, who was walking a little behind them, called out: "You must have a birthday drink tonight. Some of my home-made cherry brandy. Don't forget to tell Paul."

An afternoon without tension.

When they entered the flat, Paul welcomed them. His face was pale. "The situation is grim," he said, "nauseating speeches by the Nazis, and the Poles are bragging of their marvellous invincible cavalry."

"The Poles have always been proud of their horses," said Frau Kranz.

15

"The German tanks will mow them down," said Paul.

"You always see the worst side of everything, don't you, Paul?" said Frau Kranz.

"You people can't face facts," Paul replied.

Frau Kranz changed the subject.

"We are going to have a birthday drink in half an hour. There is no need for either of you to change," she said light-heartedly.

The brothers went to their room. As Paul had already left the house when the birthday letter arrived in the morning, Martin gave it to him now to read. While Paul was reading it, Martin was looking for the clover. It was not in the envelope. Martin searched for it on the floor, on the window-sill, on the table.

It could not be found. It was lost.

Martin knocked at Frau Kranz's door:

"The clover my mother sent — I can't find it."

But she had not seen it.

"Perhaps the maid has shaken the tablecloth out of the window?" Frau Kranz could not understand what all the fuss was about. A little leaf. Surely, it was not a great loss.

Martin went downstairs, and looked for it in the street, on the pavement.

There was no clover.

Martin was full of rage and grief.

When they were all together toasting him, he could not bear it any longer. He shouted at Frau Kranz:

"You are to blame. Nobody should have touched anything in our room." He walked quickly out of the room and wept.

"Now we shall not get to England," he whispered to himself and when Paul joined him later, reprimanding him for his inexcusable behaviour and reminding him that he was now nineteen and no more a child, Martin only replied, drained of emotion: "I lost all hope."

Paul, the big brother patted his head. "I have lost hope weeks ago, Martin."

*　　*　　*　　*

"You'd better get up. There is a commotion in the street."

16

"Why? What time is it?"

"We heard some bangs. Sounded like explosions. People say that war has started. Of course, these explosions could be part of this ridiculous air-raid exercise."

But the droning of the planes, the army lorries in the street, and a distant siren, indicated something more macabre.

Groups of people stood together, talking agitatedly. But nobody seemed to know what was happening.

The brothers walked quickly to the Refugee Centre. A crowd of anxious-looking men and women had gathered in the yard behind the building, hoping for someone to come and direct them.

Martin did not find it easy to walk through the people to get into the house. (Because he could type he had for some time helped here with clerical work.)

"You there," somebody shouted, "you are on the Committee. You should know what this is all about."

Martin tried to explain that he was only doing some clerical work and that he knew as little as anybody else. But the people were frantic. They did not listen to him.

"Are the Germans coming?"

"Where shall we go?"

"Who is going to take us away from here?"

"The Germans will kill us all."

"I am trying to find out what is happening," Martin shouted, "if you will let me pass."

"I bet he knows more than he wants to tell us," a man was calling out.

"Let me get in," Martin pleaded.

At last he stood in front of the back door. Someone unlocked it from inside. Members of the Committee were talking in the passage with subdued voices. The expressions in their faces were strained. They looked at him as if he could save the situation with one word. Martin shrugged his shoulders.

One of them said to him: "We don't know yet whether war has been declared. Come with us to the British Consulate. You'd better take something to write on with you."

Blau, the chairman, said: "I shall have to tell them outside that they must wait and that we shall keep them informed."

17

Somebody came running from another room: "Telephone call. Young men are wanted to dig trenches in the outskirts of the town."

On the way out, Martin spotted Paul. Passing him, he said: "No news yet. Back in the flat in two hours."

At the Consulate there was chaos. Everyone was bustling about, carrying files and boxes. A fire had been lit in a large bin in the middle of a room full of smoke. Bits of ashen paper floated in the air like snow.

Martin watched the turmoil with disbelief. It was all so unreal. Blau, who had gone to make some inquiries returned. "It is serious," he said, "the Consulate is being disbanded and will move later to Warsaw. All refugees are advised to make their way there. A train will be available to take some of them, women, children, the old and the sick to Kielce. All the others have got to walk there."

Martin asked: "How far away is Kielce?"

"A hundred kilometres or a little more. Those who go by train will have to wait there till the others arrive. And then we shall make further arrangements."

Blau turned to somebody else.

"The train leaves at two. I am getting back to tell everybody. Committee members will travel by train. Only essential papers are to be taken. We shall meet at the station half past one." Looking at Martin he said: "See you in Kielce."

War had been declared.

*   *   *   *

My parents over protected me when I was a child. I had never been responsible for anything. My parents did not hold with their children carrying burdens. Anxieties were kept away from us. We were never allowed to make decisions. Suddenly we were confronted with a world which was breaking at its seams.

A few days ago I was walking with Ursel on my birthday afternoon, elated, happy, hopeful. Soon we would be together with the parents. For once I had forgotten my disfigured face. I drank in the summer and the sun. The nagging fears I had suppressed.

18

With one stroke everything around me had changed.

I was in charge.

Walking at night outside the house, I was protecting Paul and Ursel and the other sleepers. My new role made me feel tall and strong. I was important.

I remember that I was glad the parents were in London, not only because they were safe, but because of the freedom their absence brought. Paul did not consciously play the part of the older brother. But I looked up to him, as in the past. We had already shared one traumatic experience: the crossing of the Czech–Polish border six months before war broke out. This had heralded what was still to come. Both of us were aware of our dependency on our parents.

In many ways Paul and I were unlike, but our love for each other held us tightly together.

We knew we needed each other.

My work with the Refugee Committee — writing out lists and copying letters — gave me a feeling of privilege. Certainly, I had no say in anything, but the mere fact that I sat in at Committee meetings, that I had knowledge of matters which could not be passed on to others, made me feel important. An indication of immaturity. But what can be expected from a very young man who had not even been trusted to buy and wear the kind of clothes he liked?

And yet, is the clover episode not an example of my childishness? Can such puerile behaviour be excused? I was not superstitious in the accepted sense. I believed in a very personal God. This belief was nurtured by a lonely and in some ways extraordinary but not unhappy childhood. Very sensitive and romantic, I had a peculiar mythical relationship with nature. The poems I wrote with great inner excitement, were offerings to my God. I only showed them to Paul who was too critical and to Georg, my friend, who thought I was a genius.

I was convinced I was 'chosen'. A very special individual. Whatever was happening to me was 'right' (for me). Even if something turned out to be disappointing, unsatisfactory, even painful. The direction I took was the only one I could

19

take. It would lead to where I was meant to go. Action was necessary. Inactivity was not wanted by my God. Of course I suffered and despaired. Often I was deeply depressed and at times hopelessness nearly suffocated me. Frequently I disbelieved, raged against fate, denied this God who was supposed to have singled me out. But my childlike faith that I would be lifted up eventually enabled me to find new strength within me.

My incompetence in dealing with the day to day practical situations was counter-balanced by this astounding trust.

Forgive me. I am already thinking ahead, thinking of our wanderings during the weeks ahead. (I did warn you that I was likely to disregard order in my narration.)

But perhaps you will understand better now, why the losing of that tiny withered clover leaf affected me as it did. I knew I had to lose it. The loss was a warning.

I fought against it, but then I accepted the foreboding in fear but also in humility.

Paul was sitting on the bed, his face drawn, his body slumped forward. "I know the news," he said to Martin, without looking up, "I did not volunteer to dig trenches. I would not have been good at it, anyway. So I walked through the town and came back here. There is war and we have to walk. It is a long way from Kattowitz to Kielce. At least the weather is fine." There was bitterness in Paul's voice.

"We have to pack some things," Martin said.

"I have already done that. I put what is absolutely necessary in a small case. We can carry it in turn. By the way, why are we going to Kielce? I have never heard of the place before."

"The plan is to get to Warsaw from there. They intend to fly us from Warsaw to London," Martin lied.

"How can they? There must be thousands of refugees like us."

Martin improvised: "I don't know. I can only think that those who've already got permits, like us, but could not get transport will go first."

Neither of them believed this.

"We'd better start off straight away," Paul said, "we are supposed to go north first and then follow the signposts to Krakow."

Martin sat down on the bed next to Paul. "Listen," he said, "I am not sure whether we can make it to Kielce. We could try to get on the train."

"Why, were you told you could? And even if you can, I can't. I'm not on the Committee like you."

"I'm not on the Committee either, as you well know. But I think we should try."

"They won't even let us on the platform."

"We can try Paul. I think Blau might help us. There was something in his face, coming from his eyes, when he said 'see you in Kielce' – I may be wrong, of course – in any case, nothing is lost if we try. If we can't get on the train, we still can start walking."

"Isn't there something dishonest about it? I mean, children and women, the old and the sick – and us?"

"And members of the Committee. Paul, we shall get on this train. I know we shall."

The brothers went to see Frau Kranz who was in tears.

"We are getting away," said Paul, "what about you?"

"Where can we go?" Frau Kranz replied, looking at Ursel who stood by the door. "We might as well stay here. The Germans will be thrown out by the Poles. Of that I am certain. But we are in for hard times. We'll sit it out, won't we, Ursel?"

Ursel did not respond.

Martin said: "We shall see you in London then . . . one day."

But the brothers never met Frau Kranz or her daughter again.

They went to Uncle Zimmermann's shop. Uncle Zimmermann was a big burly man who always had been in good humour, making jokes and laughing too loudly. Now he stood silent near the cash register.

"Boys," he said, "this means finis. Whatever is going to

happen, it is the end of life for us as we knew it. You better get away as quickly as you can."

He gave Paul some money.

Uncle Loeb, whose shop was nearby, was just bolting the glass door.

"We shall drive to Warsaw," he said, "I'm sorry I can't take you. The car is full."

Paul said that they were also going to Warsaw.

"I'll see you there."

He too gave money to Paul.

The railway station was very crowded. It seemed as if the whole town had assembled here in order to catch a train, any train. Paul said that it was useless even to try to find out from which platform the train to Kielce was going. Martin looked around to see whether there were any familiar faces. He knew many refugees by sight. Suddenly he took Paul by the hand and they followed a woman with a case. They squeezed themselves through the mass of people. At a barrier, the woman opened her handbag and showed the guard a piece of paper. She was let through. The boys watched her from a distance. Then they remained motionless. They did not know what to do. Paul said:

"It's no use, Martin. We'll never get through here. Never." But Martin looked beyond the gate. A long way off the woman was boarding the train. Then Martin spotted Blau. He was leaning out of a carriage door, looking in his direction. Blau waved. He beckoned. Martin lifted his arm. More people pushed through the gate. The guard was helpless. His shouts were being ignored. Pressures came from all sides. Then the brothers found themselves on the platform. Martin was dragging Paul forward. A carriage door was opened.

"So you made it," said Blau with a hint of a smile.

*   *   *   *

Neither Uncle Zimmermann nor Uncle Loeb were our real uncles. We had never heard of either of them before we got to Kattowitz in May that year. They were both my father's

22

distant relatives, German Jews, who settled for business reasons on the other side of the border, in Poland.

My father was born in a little town in Posen, which originally belonged to Germany but later became Polish. Geography and history are rather confusing.

My 'real' uncles and aunts — brothers and sisters of my father (my mother was an only child), all lived in Silesia, either Breslau, the Silesian capital, where I was born, or in small towns not far away. Except Aunt Flora, the widow who lived in the States. She had been married to Uncle Werner, my father's youngest brother and the only one my father had been fond of. Uncle Werner had died of cancer when he was still young. My father often spoke of him with affection.

There were Uncle Joseph, the eldest, and Uncle Benjamin and Uncle Simon (with whom my father had not been on speaking terms until fairly recently and whom we children rarely met), the kind, soft spoken Uncle David who had died of a brain tumour some years ago, Aunt Hilda — a forbidding old lady, Aunt Gerda and Aunt Elise whom I liked best of all. She was warm and motherly and always had a gleam in her eyes. I have no fond memories of any of the others, with the exception, perhaps, of Uncle David, who looked like my father and whom I had never heard saying a cross word.

All my uncles and aunts were business men and women, and I don't think they were much interested in anything else but their incomes and outgoings. They all attended the synagogue services regularly, I am sure.

My father, Leo, was different from them. He was a dreamer, not really interested in business, clever with his hands, a bit of an artist, regarded as a failure. When he was a young man, he wanted to study interior design at the technical college, but his brothers put a stop to such an outlandish plan. When my father some time later suggested he would like to become a dental technician, I can imagine that Uncle Joseph suggested Leo should see a psychiatrist. Finally my father fell in with the plans his brothers made for him to manage a shop. In his spare time he lost a lot of money on horses. He also had some wild ideas on how to make money. He never made any.

23

He met and married Sarah, my mother, an intelligent educated young woman with an interest in cultural matters. She was only accepted by the family Rosen because of her not insubstantial dowry, which was certainly a useful asset. My uncles and aunts did not like my mother. She was an outsider, like Leo, only more so. She preferred reading novels to checking accounts. She was hardly ever seen in the gallery of the synagogue. Her extraordinary taste in dresses did not meet with the approval of my uncles and aunts. She liked the theatre and went to concerts and operas. At one time she wanted to become a singer herself. I have a suspicion that the quarrel between my father and Uncle Simon started because my mother, who was never very diplomatic in her dealings with people, accused him and all the others of narrow-mindedness. I can't remember having ever spoken to Uncle Simon. When we met Aunt Selma, his wife, from time to time, with her tall good looking daughters, Uncle Simon was always absent. He certainly never entered our house. Just before we emigrated from Germany to Czechoslovakia, mother told us that father had made it up with Uncle Simon.

All my uncles and aunts escaped the holocaust and settled down in various parts of the world, with the exception of Uncle Joseph, a stiff unbending man who remained in Breslau throughout the war but survived it. He died a natural death at the age of ninety-four in the late forties. His loyal wife, Linda, a former salesgirl in his shop, whom he had married soon after the death of his first wife, was a gentile. She became Jewish. She kept him hidden in an attic throughout the war years, pretending that her Jewish husband had left Germany before the war and assuming the role of an Aryan woman who had learnt her lesson. She found work in a factory and cared for the old man, living a lonely life somewhere near the roof of a house. I only hope he expressed his gratitude to her in some way before he died.

Paul and I did not look forward to the occasions when we had to visit our uncles and aunts. We visited because we had to. Dressed in our blue or white sailor suits with long white stockings and shining patent leather shoes, we were looked over, patted on the head and asked to sit where all the other nieces and nephews sat, away from the grown-ups, who were

24

too busy with their own affairs to take much notice of us. We were well fed. Hot chocolate and huge quantities of home-made cakes. We played very quiet games. The grown-ups must not be disturbed. From time to time an aunt came over to us and asked whether we had enough to eat, or brought some sweets in a little silver dish. The time came to leave, to our relief. We bowed, shook hands, said "thank you". Bored but glad it was over, we left the house and prayed the next visit would be a long time off.

But the visits to Aunt Elise and Aunt Gerda were different. They did not live in Breslau. They had married shopkeepers in small towns. Paul and I went to see them on rare occasions. Although neither Münsterberg nor Striegau were exciting places, any journey, however short, thrilled me. And I did like the quaintness of these communities where people seemed to know each other. So unlike Breslau, where even your neighbours remained strangers. Breslau, which I never got to know, but for the southern part of the city where we lived. Aunt Gerda, the 'Münsterberg Aunt' was a little formal in her manner and neither she nor her husband had much idea how to occupy young children, but we went for walks with their two sons, older than us, and sometimes I was allowed to help in the shop. Once, I remember, I caused havoc with the till and to my deep disappointment I was then not permitted to play being the cashier. But it was the radio they had which fascinated me most of all. The loudspeaker was standing on the top shelf of a bookcase in the lounge. With the accompaniment of much hissing, crackling and whistling, voices came from nowhere and I recall there was plenty of piano music by Chopin. The radio station was not far away, across the border in Poland. On a table stood large heavy accumulators, and there were green web-like aerials of all sizes which Paul was permitted to assemble in order to obtain the different stations.

But my favourite Aunt Elise and Uncle Robert, who always tried to make me laugh, and the ever cheerful Cousin Tilda, lived in Striegau. I felt more at ease with them than with my parents. They were also the only relatives who appreciated that it was not only Paul who was musical. On my last visit there — I was already in Grammar School — they

b

happened to hear me play on their upright one of my little compositions. Black keys only. And then I sang:

"My song is not in major
neither in minor . . ."

It became clear that the dears were not very musical themselves. They not only praised me, but thought I had considerable talent. I felt that I had been accepted at last, not just as the ugly younger brother of the exceptionally bright Paul, but as the highly-gifted nephew Martin. Indeed, it was a glorious occasion.

*　　*　　*　　*

After our arrival in Kattowitz, we lived at first with the family Zimmermann, but took it in turns to have our meals with them or with the Loebs, who lived nearby. The Zimmermanns were warm, friendly people who welcomed us like long lost friends, although they had only met my father many years ago. They were tall, burly, even fat. One of their main pleasures in life was eating well. They did. Even Paul who never took much interest in food, admitted that the cooking was fabulous.

Every other day I had to go to the Loebs to eat with them. It almost seemed as if Uncle and Aunt Loeb wanted to teach me a lesson. Midday meals consisted mainly of potatoes and cottage cheese. Sometimes there was some kind of hash. The pudding was stewed fruit. There were long and heated discussions at table, about politics, the possible war between Germany and Poland, Thomas Mann and Byron. It all went over my head. I preferred the less cultured, simple, generous Zimmermanns across the way. And I liked to eat well.

I was saddened when after a few weeks arrangements were made for Paul and me to stay with Frau Kranz. But the Zimmermanns had new guests. A couple from Berlin. She was tall, bejewelled and rather beautiful. He suffered from a double rupture and could hardly move. She complained about his impotence. He advised her to find another man until he had had his operation. Uncle and Aunt Zimmermann listened carefully to their bickering and then suggested a game of cards. Playing cards was the main recreational

26

activity in this household.

We never found out what happened to the Zimmermanns. They probably did not survive the war. The Loebs managed to flee to Romania and later emigrated to Palestine.

What gave me the idea of trying to get on the train with Paul? I don't know. It is doubtful whether we would have been able to reach Kielce by foot. We learnt later that many refugees were injured or killed during the walk. None of us knew then, of course, of the great speed of the German invasion. Was it immoral for Paul and me to join the women and children, the old and the sick and the members of the Committee? I feel no guilt.

It is Blau we have to thank, for letting us board the train. Blau's intervention probably saved our lives.

We have all travelled in overcrowded trains in great discomfort for short distances. The journey from Kattowitz to Kielce would normally not take longer than a few hours. On this occasion it took from early afternoon to the evening of the day after the next. I cannot recall much of the journey. After travelling a few kilometres the train stopped. Again and again it stopped. The train was often attacked by planes. We moved into sidings and remained there for hours. Apparently forgotten. Paul and I took turns sitting on the small suitcase we had brought with us. We sat in the corridor. We whispered in German to each other for fear of antagonising the other passengers. Not all of them were refugees. Bodies and boxes everywhere. Bodies and boxes. Then there was the stench coming from the toilet. There was no water for flushing. We pleaded silently with the people to let us get to it, but there was hardly any room to move. You squeezed and squeezed. You used your arms and elbows. Somebody had to give way.

We must have got some food from somewhere. I don't think we could have managed without it for two days. But it was the thirst which I remember. I was always thirsty.

Suddenly the train whistled and halted abruptly. Planes. We rushed out into the open, ran down the embankment and took shelter in a ditch. There were bombs and machine-gun fire. There was the glow of flames. "A container with petrol has been hit," somebody said.

One night we stopped in the station at Krakau. There was very heavy bombardment. It was the first time that I saw casualties being carried away on stretchers.

We have often seen the plight of refugees on television. But feelings cannot be televised. To be one of a large group of people driven by compulsion to get away before it is too late. To want to be propelled forward. To hope that all was a dream. To pray for release, release from fear, from terror.

A few hundred feet above us were the German planes, their physical closeness struck panic in us. They were like threatening colossal birds and the whistling of the falling bombs sounded as if they were laughing at us.

During the journey, a thin elderly man recognised Martin. He managed to wind himself through the bizarre mass and faced the boy. He was excited, his face was flushed, his eyes looked wild.

"Young Rosen," he said, controlling his voice with difficulty, "so you managed to get on the train. And with your brother, I see. Well done, Rosen. Well done. But you are not really a member of the Committee, are you? Not really. I know, you helped. You only helped with the typing. And now, I am going to tell you something. Young Rosen, listen. Listen carefully. Listen to me," — his voice had become manacing — "my son is walking. You understand? Walking. He must be your age. But he is not on the train. He is walking. I shall wait for him in Kielce. If he does not arrive, young Rosen, if he can't make it, if anything should happen to him, I shall kill you. I shall kill you. You too will not survive."

I do not know whether father and son were reunited.

28

The train arrived in Kielce in the evening. Wearily we assembled in the station yard and started to walk into the town. Sirens were screaming. There was the biting smell and taste of burning everywhere. We saw the split houses which stood like animals whose bellies had been ripped open. Flames danced amongst the beams of many roofs. The brothers looked around. It was all so incredible, as if one walked in a place dreamt up, barely imagined, outside any experience. 'Perhaps everything will dissolve at any moment, if one only could will it enough,' Martin thought. 'This will never become part of me, certainly, it is happening, I know that, but I am outside it, I am looking at it but what I see cannot touch me. I am not part of it, I am removed from it.'

They came to the cinema. The cinema was filled with people who had seated themselves in the auditorium, talking animatedly but quietly to each other. Martin wondered where they had all come from. He did not know that many had come from other parts of the country, hoping for transport to the capital. Warsaw was bound to be safe. One could wait for the end of the war in Warsaw. Some young people who had walked, told stories of German ambushes and even atrocities. Nobody wanted to believe them.

"There was a shepherd boy," somebody said. "He was looking after some sheep. I saw a plane dropping from the sky, diving, and then bullets rained. The boy fell. People came and carried him away."

"I saw a German soldier molesting a woman peasant," said another. But there could not be any German soldiers in Poland. What about the defences? The famous invincible cavalry? The Polish air force? What about the acclaimed valour of the Polish army? No, he must be mistaken. There were no Germans in Poland.

'A cinema,' Martin thought, 'yesterday, perhaps, they came to watch Greta Garbo or the Marx Brothers. They cried and laughed, because they recognised something of themselves in what was happening on the screen. One looked and got involved, but an hour later there was nothing left, inside

29

all was blank. Like me. I feel empty.'

A man said: "There is a meeting of the group leaders."

Paul said: "You mean, they will tell us where we have got to run to from here?"

"You did not run," the other replied, "I saw you coming from the station. I walked thirty kilometres today. I don't feel like marching any further tonight."

'He is trying to make us feel guilty,' Martin thought.

Suddenly Paul's face lit up: "I don't believe my eyes," he exclaimed, "Rudi and Ernst. Rudi and Ernst here."

Rudi and Ernst were two former friends who had been in the same form as Paul at school in Breslau.

Surprise. They agreed it would be helpful to stay together. Another young man whom Rudi and Ernst had met when they sheltered in a barn was introduced to the brothers. Franz looked the toughest of the five, Rudi had the same build as Paul, slim and still boyish, and stocky little Ernst looked weatherbeaten and tanned as if he had just come from a holiday.

Martin was the youngest. He thought: 'There are enough of us now to make decisions. But I don't have to make any. I shall just do what the others do. That suits me.'

There was no more news that evening. The group found a corner in the foyer of the cinema. Their jackets became pillows.

Early next morning they were awakened by shouts.

"Everybody to the auditorium," somebody announced.

Soon they all looked at the platform as if a performance was about to start.

A man entered from the left wing and Martin smiled: 'The film can't be shown after all. There is a delay.'

"I am sorry I have got bad news." The man was not acting.

'Perhaps the reel got lost,' thought Martin.

"The Nazis have broken through the defences. We must get away as quickly as we can."

There was no panic. No scenes. No screaming. Some weeping. Some hand-wringing.

A few left the cinema immediately, probably with no idea

what to do next.

Martin had given the group a name: the quintet. The quintet decided not to rush matters and await further developments.

Blau passed on to Martin a heap of papers: old lists and notes which it would be best to destroy. In the yard bonfires had been lit. Papers were frantically torn up and thrown into the flames. Martin joined a group. Thin black skins floated through the air.

'This is the second time I am witnessing a small auto-da-fé,' he thought. Then the bombardment of the town started again.

He disposed of the material.

He ran into the building. All the glass vibrated.

'Even the glass trembles in fear,' he thought, 'everything is being destroyed: paper and wood and brick. Everything becomes nothing.'

When the all-clear sounded, the quintet left the cinema and went to a small restaurant where they were the only guests. It was to be their last proper meal for a very long time. They agreed to stay another night at the cinema and leave the following morning.

The sun was rising. It was going to be a beautiful summer's day. The sky gleamed gold and red.

'What are we doing to all the glory around us?' Martin thought.

The boys turned round. Kielce was burning. Above the town there was a blanket of thick dirty blackish smoke.

'Two skies,' thought Martin, 'two skies getting ready for battle. Which sky will win?'

*   *   *   *

We did not deprive anybody by getting on the train. But we caused resentment. The poor man's hope for his son's safe arrival was now flavoured with a hate for us, who had disobeyed the order and had come by train.

31

I was already aware at that time that there is no meeting with others, however fleeting, which is merely coincidental. Perhaps we are more tied to each other than we dare to admit. If his son was killed on the way, would his father ever forgive us?

We have all witnessed people in distress. But it is not possible to feel as they do. We can not experience their experience. You describe what happened. The other says: "How awful. Did it really happen?" You assure him. It has taken place. You were there. Nothing has been exaggerated. But it was your personal drama. It belongs to you in its uniqueness. Is it possible to share it with somebody else?

Walking into the town after the dramatic train journey. The shells of houses, the singed trees, the grieving people. It was happening outside. I had lost myself. I was mourning for my loss. I was like a particle driven somewhere, a projectile forced in an unknown direction. From that moment on, the inner drama took over and embraced me. Everything I saw, I saw as through a veil which seemed to dim the world. Paul was with me, but I was very much on my own.

It was odd that a cinema offered us shelter. Since we had left Breslau over two years ago, films had become important. Living in Brünn with the parents, in two small rooms, in a very tense atmosphere — when carefully thought out future plans (or so we imagined) did not materialise because they were usually without any realistic foundation — created pressures. Pressures which were difficult to bear. To go to a little cinema in Czechoslovakia was very cheap. Even I could afford the one krone entrance fee. I could lose myself in the darkness and watch the action on the screen, so unrelated to my own life. Adventures, love stories, thrillers, musicals: anything would do. Any drug. If only to get away for an hour or two from the hopeless arguments within the family. Occasionally I was able to persuade my parents to join me. Then I felt jubilant. For once it was possible to be together for the joy of it, instead of using each other for the pain of it.

32

What an extraordinary chance to have met up with Rudi and Ernst. Paul had not seen them since his schooldays over four years ago when all three were sitting for their higher matriculation at the Johannes Gymnasium in Breslau. I only knew them by sight, watching them in the school yard. They were always engaged in serious discussions. Rudi lived in the same district as we did. His father was a respected pharmacist. His mother suffered from an inborn hip disease and could walk only with great difficulty. I avoided watching her. Rudi was a communist, I knew. I could not understand this. I hardly understood what a communist was. I thought only working class people were communists. The men who delivered the coal or the plumber or the chimney sweep. "How can a boy from a well-to-do family be a communist?" my mother had asked Paul once.

"He is not the only young Jewish intellectual with strong leftish convictions," Paul had replied.

Ernst belonged to a different set of people. His parents were orthodox Jews and the devout families kept to themselves and had no dealings with us, the so-called 'liberals'. We too felt that we had nothing in common with them.

Franz was the outsider. His family had lived in the 'Sudetenland' that part of Czechoslovakia inhabited mostly by Germans. When the Germans moved into the 'Sudetenland' after the 1938 Munich agreement, Franz's father was taken to a concentration camp. Franz never heard from him. His mother moved to Prague. A few days before the war, Franz crossed the border to Poland. He was the most practically minded of the 'quintet'.

We had become a group. Our aim was not to get caught by the Germans, to make it to Warsaw and then to England.

How relieved I was not to have to struggle alone with Paul. I was still suffering from the memory of the nightmarish border-crossing a few months before. Nothing could happen now which was more torturing than that particular week. If only we had not been on our own then, I thought, if only we had belonged to a group with someone to lead us, if only we could have followed instructions: how much easier everything would have been.

*   *   *   *

We had left Germany at the beginning of 1937, full of hopes for the future. My father had plans to start an export business with Great Britain. We settled in Brünn, in Moravia, not far from the Austrian border. Germans and Czechs lived in this pretty town. Brünn was different from Breslau which I had never loved.

We had some money at first — my mother's jewels had been smuggled to England and sold there — there was enough to live on for the time being until my father's business affairs began to show profits. The future looked bright.

Paul was to continue his medical studies in Prague and because I had learnt to use the typewriter and could do shorthand, I became my father's unpaid clerk.

The export business did not materialise. My father travelled to London once or twice, promises were made to him, samples of stockings were ordered and that was the end of that. He tried other things. Inventions of his and others were bound to be in demand and would bring in a lot of money. I remember a particular filter which, installed in a car would reduce consumption. A small crippled man had made a prototype. He came to our flat and assured us that soon we would be able to buy our own house. The invention was tested by independent examiners and found to be useless. There was the glove, a kind of mitten made of wool with some dry boot polish at the end of it. Uncle Robert from Striegau whose brainchild this new product was, came specially to Brünn to discuss the distribution. Unfortunately shoes and boots were being scratched by the hard mould. The project was dropped. My father designed a tidy tray made of stiff corrugated paper. It was meant to be sent to customers by firms for advertising purposes. Nobody was interested. My father met a woman who had a chicken farm outside the town. She had invented a pocket ready reckoner. It had already been patented years ago by someone else. There was also a new type of fountain pen on which my father had worked for many weeks. But he could not stop it from

34

leaking.

If only his original plan, the export of hosiery, had met with success! At least he knew something of this merchandise which he had sold in his shop in Germany. When father went to London we awaited his return with excitement. Would he bring home orders? He was always optimistic — perhaps he only pretended.

"Everybody liked me in London," he told us.

"Did they like the goods?" asked my mother.

"They liked the goods and the price. They want one dozen of the type 'B' stockings and two dozen of type 'L'."

"Were they satisfied with the terms of delivery?" My mother had learnt by now some of the jargon.

"They are well satisfied. You wait, the orders will roll in soon. Have no doubt about it. All will be well."

My poor father. How he was waiting for the postman day by day, waiting for him in the street even when it was raining, his cigar hanging cold from his lips, then coming into the flat, comforting my mother, comforting himself that the promised large order was on the way.

But the orders never came.

Once my mother saw him coming out of a betting shop.

"It's all right," he said to her before she had time to reproach him, "I only put a few kronen on a horse. An outsider with a good family history. He is likely to win."

I was with mother and pleaded with her not to start a row in front of all these people.

Oh, these quarrels! Sometimes my father wept when he felt everyone was against him. "Nothing I ever do is right," he cried, "nothing comes off. And then I'm blamed by my wife and sons." And turning to me he shouted: "And haven't you always had enough to eat, Martin?"

And then he came up with another plan, another possibility, another opportunity to make money.

"This has never been done before," he said, "it is new, quite new."

But nobody was waiting for anything my father suggested, organised or built himself.

35

I can still hear my mother complaining:

"He has always been irresponsible. He always tried the wrong things. He can't provide for his family. He never could. Even in Breslau everything was a struggle. We pretended to be well-to-do. We never were. Your father lives on hopes. Nothing has come of anything he started. His schemes are built on air. Of course, he should have become a dental mechanic. But no, he had to listen to his fine brothers. They wanted him to go into business. But he is not made to be a businessman. Look where we are now. I have not got enough housekeeping money to do the shopping. What on earth made me marry him? I know he wanted me because I was chaste. He wanted a pure woman to be the mother of his children. And I was too stupid to say no. I had loved a chemist. No, your grandfather said, no, he is not good enough for my daughter. And look where I am now. In a foreign country with no prospects, no prospects at all. And my husband goes for a walk and spends his last krone on horses. Life has not treated me well. I'm sure I don't deserve all this misery."

My mother had no control over herself. She would talk like this in front of her sons.

She had been punished. Why should she not punish her children?

I clung to Paul although he did not live with us but stayed in Prague. His medical studies he had to give up. There was not enough money to pay for them. Still, I thought, he was luckier than I. At least he could live his own life amongst his friends. He did not have to bear the stress which sometimes oppressed me so much that I had to escape into the woods near the town or into a cinema. I clung to Paul. I could write to him about my feelings, my difficulties with the parents. His replies I treasured. He understood and warmed me with his concern. If it had not been for him, I am sure, I would have lost all stability. His letters and those from my friends Georg and Toni who both still lived in Breslau, sustained me. Georg I loved because I knew he loved me. Toni represented everything I was not: he was a scout, energetic, independent, had plenty of common sense. He was a born survivor.

36

All these letters expressed belief in me, belief in my talent as a poet, belief in my ability to find strength within me during this bewildering period of my life.

It was difficult to keep the letters away from my parents. There was no drawer I could lock up. My mother was convinced it was her right to read the mail addressed to me.

She said to me once: "How would I know otherwise, whether you got mixed up in something you shouldn't?"

I had to hide them, even burn them. They were so personal, so intimate. I feared my mother. She would read something into them. She would say that the love Georg and I felt for each other was unnatural. She would be tactless and sarcastic. My father would be forced to take sides: "You should not keep secrets from your parents."

Of course, most letters I could easily have given them to read, particularly those which did not make any reference to them or contained little else but factual information. But I was an adolescent in rebellion, a rebellion in particularly stressful circumstances.

I wanted to get away from them.

I did not want to have anything to do with them.

I had never been close to them as a child.

Now my parents had become hateful to me.

Two opportunities arose during our last year in Brünn, when separation was a possibility. But neither of the opportunities was taken. In spite of all the misgivings and distrust, the ties were too strong.

Why I attended the Maccabi Youth Club for a time, I cannot remember. I must have met someone who invited me to a meeting, because I had never been a Zionist. On the contrary. I aped Paul who made it clear to everyone how steeped we were in German culture. "Never mind the Nazis," he said, "we are Germans and will remain Germans. Goethe, Schiller, Beethoven, Mozart: They are our inheritance. We are not prepared to give up what we have inherited. Rightfully inherited by birth. There is no Jewish nation. Of course, we are Jews. We would not deny it. But there can be no nation of Jews who bring with them a variety of different cultures."

I had hardly read any Goethe or Schiller and was only mildly attracted to classical music at the time. I certainly had no understanding of German culture. But Paul's views must also be my views.

"Why should we work for a 'State of Jewry'?" I declared at the Maccabi meeting. "We are German Jews or Czech Jews or Austrian Jews. What sort of culture will there be in Palestine when we bring to it everything which has become part of us in the different countries we have come from? What can possibly be created out of such a culture clash."

'Culture clash,' I thought, 'that sounds good: culture clash.' Then a little voice inside me was asking: 'What does it mean?' After such a sermon I expected to be asked not to come back. To my surprise, however, it was put to me that I seriously consider going to one of the training centres in Denmark with a view to eventual immigration to Palestine. I protested:

"I am not a Zionist. Why do you think I should go to Palestine?"

"It's young people like you we need, Martin," was the reply. "We need youngsters who can think, who do not just follow the flag. You provide the money for the fare, we shall see to everything else."

But we had no funds and my parents did not want to part from me.

September 1938. The Germans occupied a piece of Czechoslovakia. Hitler was following us. I recall the night of the total blackout. My mother and I stood by the window, looking into the darkness. We expected to hear the sound of planes. But there was only a frightening silence. My father was in bed, apparently asleep. "There is nothing any of us can do," he had said while getting undressed, "we might just as well go to bed."

"There you see," my mother said to me. "This is typical of your father. When one needs support, he can't give it. I am glad you are with me, Martin . . . Do you think Paul is all right?"

"The Germans are not occupying Prague," I said.

My father was probably happy that for once, matters had been taken out of his hands. He could not be expected to find a solution.

Next morning we were relieved to hear that war had not broken out. But we guessed that it would only be a matter of time before the Nazis took over the whole country. We had to get out of the country. But how? And where to?

Father wrote to his nephew Bruno in London. My cousin Bruno was a clever man. He had studied law in Breslau, obtained his doctorate, was involved in some minor student rebellion and had to disappear quickly. (The Nazis were on their way to power.) After a short time in Switzerland he emigrated to England, studied once more, got his PhD, became a barrister, started his own law practice and was appointed professor at the London University. Bruno was clever and successful. He wrote back after a few weeks saying that he was going to make some enquiries. Perhaps it would be possible for us to come to England.

In the meantime we heard that Nicaragua was accepting refugees. But sufficient funds were necessary. We did not have any money. What about the United States? Their 'quota' was filled. Australia: They wanted young people prepared to work on the land. Or those with special skills.

"No letter from Bruno yet?"

"He is probably already making the necessary arrangements," my father said with his usual optimism, "otherwise we would have heard from him by now."

"But Leo," (this formal address was a sign of my mother's annoyance) "as usual you are living in a fool's paradise. Bruno was never very fond of us and you know it. Why should he want to go out of his way to help us?"

"Bruno is a pious Jew," father said, "his father is my brother after all."

"That is no reason why he should put himself out for us," replied mother.

"Besides," father continued, "if it had not been for us, he would be without a wife. It was through us that he met Sonia in London because it is we who arranged . . . "

"Sh . . . Sh . . . " my mother interrupted, "he doesn't know that. Neither does Martin."

I was shocked by what had been implied. I did not know then that many marriages were arranged at that time to make it possible for young Jewish women to get out of Germany.

No country, we were told, would accept us unless we possessed some practical skill. We had to use our hands profitably. Plumbers, carpenters, tilers, electricians, land-workers: they would be permitted to immigrate. One had to get trained in something. Even if one had started studying for some profession, like Paul who intended to become a doctor, one had to throw such ideas out of one's mind. Special vocational committees set up courses for young and not so young people. Paul wrote from Prague that he had enlisted for a course in welding. Not enough people had as yet applied. Later he decided to become an electrician. I could not imagine him standing on a ladder and wiring a room. He, with his intellect, his critical faculties, he, the brain of the family, the future professor, *he* was to repair fuses?

I suffered for him as I have suffered for him on so many occasions since. But according to his letters, the course did not cause him much agony. I think he regarded his new occupation as rather a joke. I did not feel I could laugh.

In the meantime there was an opportunity for me to join a short course in carpentry. It was held in a small factory not far from where we lived in Brünn and was run by the two proprietors, the brothers Guttenberg. After six months, the trainees would be sufficiently skilled to carry out the more routine jobs. That is what Herr Guttenberg, the younger of the two, told us. We were standing in our new overalls behind the benches.

The next weeks were very unhappy ones. I hated the atmosphere of the workshop. I hated the fishy smell of glue. I hated the foreman, he either told dirty jokes or made sarcastic remarks. I hated wood, the feel of wood, its shape, its resistance to me. I hated the dark freezing early mornings, the yard where the planks — so lovingly stacked — had to be lifted with stiff fingers and moved with awkward gestures into the building. But most of all, I hated my hands. It was the first time I realised that I was unable to use them. Again and again I tried desperately to make a simple joint. But the two pieces never fitted. I could not saw along a straight line. I hated the tools. I hated my hands on the tools. Then the machinery in the mill. Screeching howling animals. Animals I had to feed. The foreman giggled: "I have got the wrong sow by its ear," he called out aloud so that all the other trainees heard him, "you'll never make a carpenter."

Paul must have found it difficult to understand the utter desolation which permeated my letters to him. I thought of leaving, running away, anywhere, away from this hell. I planned my escape. But I did not leave. Whenever I could, I went for lone walks along the wintry streets.

I wrote a short cycle of poems: 'The Songs of a Great Torment'. Misery can be comforting.

As the weeks went by, wretchedness gave way to resignation. I knew now I would never become a carpenter. I had learnt that there are limitations in us which one has to accept. The lesson in carpentry had had its uses. I had learnt to accept myself with a little humility.

One of the trainees was Lieberfeld. He had studied economics but had given up his studies. He was a very slim young man, already quite bald, with long delicate fingers. A slight smile never left his face. I talked to him about my clumsiness, which he must have witnessed, and also mentioned to him that I wrote poetry. (Strange, because I rarely let anybody know.) He invited me to his house one evening and asked me to read out some of my efforts. He listened with great attention. He was extremely courteous. His comments were both helpful and encouraging.

"You may not be able to do carpentry," he said, "but you have other gifts. You must develop them."

When it was time to leave, he went to a shelf, took a book

41

from it. He inscribed his name on the fly sheet and handed it to me.

It was a bible. I have still got it. I wonder what happened to Lieberfeld. I knew him for such a short time. But he was very dear to me.

When I arrived home that night, my mother was waiting up for me.

"Where have you been?" she shouted because she had been worried. "It is after one in the morning. As long as you live here with us, you will be home at a reasonable hour."

I did not mind what she said.

I felt that the world belonged to me.

There was another trainee, a little younger than I. He possessed the gift of beauty. He looked as I imagined a boy from Greece to look: tall and brown with well-defined features, dark eyes, bushy eyebrows, black hair. But it was not merely his looks I was attracted to. I loved watching him work. He moved with grace. I wanted to talk to him, make friends with him. But I was aware of my own ugliness and kept on observing him from a distance.

And then suddenly, after barely three months when the snow began to melt, the course ended. The firm was busy with a new product — large transport cases ordered by potential emigrants for their belongings. The Jews in Brünn knew that it could not be long before the Nazis invaded. Travel agencies, foreign consulates and refugee organisations were being beleaguered. There were no hasty departures, but people were getting ready.

We still had not heard anything definite from my cousin Bruno. In his last letters he warned us to be patient. Home Office decisions took a very long time. There was nothing else to do but wait. There were no other possibilities.

I knew that one could get to Palestine illegally. Transports were being arranged from time to time. Apart from paying the passage, one could leave everything to the organisers. With the Nazi threat becoming more pressing every day, my parents could not object any more. The Germans might be here the next day. I had to get the money for the fare from somewhere. But how?

I cannot recall who suggested that I knock at the houses of well known rich Jewish people. The idea seemed to be so outlandish. But here I was, ringing door bells or walking into stores, begging for money, explaining that I wanted to get to Palestine.

It is difficult for me now to understand how I was able to stand in front of strangers, telling them of my plight and asking for a contribution. Perhaps it was the actor in me, the clown who took charge. Usually shy, even withdrawn, afraid of people (and what they might think about my face), I now degraded myself. Without pride, without shame. Once, when I was given only a few kronen, I walked to the nearest butcher, bought a pound of sausages and returned to the house of the stingy benefactor. He opened the door and I can hear myself saying:

"I brought you this. You obviously are in greater need than I." I gave him the sausages wrapped up in newspaper and ran down the stairs quickly.

My face is blushing as I am telling you this.

Of course, I did not collect enough money for the journey. Once again I did not take the opportunity to break away from the parents. I handed over the few notes to my father. They helped to pay the guide a few months later to take us across the border to Poland.

I was not sorry to have missed the transport to Palestine. The parting from Paul would have been too painful.

Two years ago I had stayed with him for a few weeks in Prague while waiting for the parents to arrive. We had arranged that the parents would come independently. It was a memorable occasion. The Nazis had been left behind.

A new life was to start.

My father's hopes for a bright future infected even my mother. Paul, of course, had his doubts. But then he always had doubts. He kept his dark thoughts to himself.

43

I was not homesick. I missed Georg and Toni but then I was hoping to see them again one day. They did say they would also emigrate to Czechoslovakia. There was nothing else I had left behind which I could miss. On the last day before my departure Georg gave me a little book. It was carefully wrapped up.

"Don't open it now," Georg pleaded, "open it when you are in the train to Prague."

When I opened it, I saw that Georg had written something in it.

> 'To my dear Martin,
> hoping,
> that all your love
> and your longing
> for your native land
>   is also love
> and great longing
>   for me.
>
>   Georg.'

I was very angry. How sentimental! How melodramatic! And why did he make this declaration for everyone to see? Was not our friendship something holy, intangible, intimate and so very personal between us that it had to shut out witnesses? And would I ever yearn for Germany, Germany which I was only too happy to leave? I tore out the sheet. But I did not destroy it. I have kept it separately in an envelope for all these years.

My anger was not justified. How prophetic his words sounded later. Hardly a day went by when I did not think then of my childhood, my friendship with Georg, our love for each other.

I had torn out his inscription because I was too small to accept his offering.

(Very recently I stuck it back into the book, where it belongs.)

Brünn – Brno in Czech – has been described in an up-to-date

brochure published by a travel organisation as a town which is 'conspicuously industrial and also an important railway junction'. It is bound to have changed since we lived there over half a century ago. It was a delightful place with its castle, the sloping mounds, the leafy parks at the edge of the town, the loveliness of the gardens. How I enjoyed the nearby woods, the rich, leafy, hilly countryside. But what beautified the place was the feeling of freedom and hope of good things to come.

"Here I would like to stay," I said to myself on the first day. "The town is small enough to get to know and large enough to get lost in."

Our first home was with Frau Binder. The house she and her daughter lived in looked stately. She was a widow with two children. Her son — we were told later — was a patient in a mental hospital. We occupied two rooms and shared the kitchen with Frau Binder. The sitting-room was almost luxuriously furnished with a baby grand piano. The put-u-up placed in the room for me was the only ugly piece of furniture. Although I had hoped to have my own room, nothing could spoil my carefree mood. Mother did her best to get on with Frau Binder.

Frau Binder was not an easy woman. She made many demands. My mother who had until then run her own household found herself dependent on someone else. Frau Binder came to our rooms when we were out, opened the windows, aired the blankets, cleaned the rooms and even polished the floor if she did not find it spotless. She did not intend to be helpful, but wanted to teach mother a lesson. One day she locked the piano. We had to wait for our meals. Frau Binder prepared hers first and left a note for mother to see: 'Please leave the kitchen as you find it.' Mother felt humiliated. Although not used to housework, she was meticulous. Frau Binder had no reason to complain. One day Frau Binder referred to us as 'you people' and when mother asked her what she meant by addressing us in this way, Frau Binder said that families who had to give up their homes, should be grateful to those who gave them shelter. My father was called in. He agreed to increase the rent. My mother blamed him for giving in. We stayed for a little while longer until it became clear that we could not afford to pay out so much regularly.

When the relationship with our landlady was still more or less agreeable, I was obliged to go to the opera one evening with her daughter. Mother had been concerned for a long time that I had no girlfriend. "It is only right that young people should get together," she said. When I was dressed to go out, she inspected me. Did my tie match the shirt? What about a handkerchief in the breast pocket? Were my shoes properly polished?

The girl was not pretty. She had spots on her face. She looked gross somehow. Her lips were very full. Pigtails were tied into a bun. Her bosom was already too abundant. I certainly was not interested in her, but on this evening I was ashamed to be seen with her. She was dressed in a flowery outfit which stressed her clumsy adolescence.

Considering what I felt about my own looks, my critical appraisal was no doubt too severe. But my mother had to be opposed. In matters so personal and important to me, I could not possibly fall in with my mother's wishes. I had not chosen the girl. Even if my evening companion had been radiant and charming, I would have hesitated to take notice of her. But she was not. We went to Puccini's *Turandot*. We pretended not to know each other. The poor girl probably despised me. My behaviour was of course quite unjustified. During the interval I went to the lavatory and stayed there until the bell rang. It was a horrible evening.

But my mother did not give up so easily. She arranged one Sunday for us all to go for a walk. Mother told me to be nice to the girl and we were left behind to walk together.

"Young people like to be by themselves," I heard mother say to Frau Binder.

But mother lost the battle. She failed to arrange a love match.

46

Frau Binder's son came home one weekend. I had dreaded the visit. A lunatic, a wild thing, a maniac. What would he do? How safe were we? How should we behave? Would we meet him in the corridor? How should we talk to him? Would he have fits? Would he scream? Attack us with a knife, perhaps? Or even with an axe? There was somebody else I had known who was said to be mentally ill. A friend of my parents. Frau Perlmutter. But she had been suffering from depressions. When you are depressed you are quiet. You are not mad when you are depressed. And Frau Perlmutter was never a patient in a mental hospital. But this boy of Frau Binder's. That was a different matter. My father had spoken to Frau Binder. He told her that it was unfair to us to have the boy here. Frau Binder just shrugged her shoulders, as if to say, don't stay here if you don't want to. Mother locked the doors.

The young crazy man was more handsome than his sister. He was less neurotic than his mother. He showed no signs of aggression. I met him outside the front door, which had been left open so that I could make a quick retreat, should the need arise.

He asked me whether I liked Brünn and advised me not to miss the 'Moravian Karst' and visit the grottos. I just stopped myself from asking him where he lived. Then his mother shouted for him in a mad way from inside the house. We just had time to smile to each other. I hoped I could see him again, but did not.

Did he become a guinea-pig during the war in one of the experiments the German doctors carried out on people with a mental illness? I often wondered.

Our contentment and happiness was affected by the death of Masaryk, the great Czech politician and philosopher. His death was a signal. Life in Czechoslovakia was in jeopardy. Could the democracy be sustained? The people mourned. Silently they stood in the 'Square of Freedom'. Would Czechoslovakia remain free?

My father's business endeavours were not successful. Our savings started to dwindle. We had to find cheaper accommodation. When we gave notice to Frau Binder she said she was very sorry. Although she had been a difficult landlady, she expressed her regret. Being an emotional woman she wiped away a tear. I was pleased that her daughter had made herself invisible.

Mother was not sorry to have to change homes. She was quite looking forward to reign in a smaller flat in a more modern house. The two rooms were indeed very small. Mine was hardly big enough to hold the couch. There was a table in my parents' room which we used for our meals. Coming out of the front door and looking to the right, a small hill, perhaps I should say: an enormous heap of earth covered with grass, seemed to have planted itself a few steps from our house. It was curious to hear and see children at play on the top. (I could imagine living amidst mountains.) Apart from the bright ringing laughter of children everything was very quiet where we lived now. There was no traffic. Our little street was a cul-de-sac. There was a restaurant at the other corner, next to a few shops. One could pretend to oneself that one lived in the country.

We christened our new landlady Fräulein Beova, (the first letter and the ending of the name of our street). I don't think I ever knew her real name. She was a small woman, in her thirties, slimly built, red hair, ("not natural, of course," my mother said,) protruding discoloured teeth. ("Why does she not have them seen to?").

My mother had met her before, of course, when my parents were looking for a flat. Unfortunately they had forgotten to make enquiries about the use of the kitchen. As there was no other room, except the bathroom, they assumed that we could occupy the whole flat. Wrong. Fräulein Beova slept in the kitchen. My parents had overlooked the narrow camp-bed under the window.

My mother was appalled. Usually the state of the kitchen was indescribable. Fräulein Beova spent much of her time in the bathroom. My mother was convinced that Fräulein Beova was a prostitute. The sexy magazines left lying about in the kitchen, the scent of cheap face-powder and the way our landlady rigged herself out in the afternoons and left the flat punctually at three o'clock with clattering very high

48

heels: enough evidence. But Fräulein never brought back her male clients. She always returned alone late in the evening or at night. She was no bother, apart from the rigorous cleaning which my mother had to do in the kitchen before starting to cook.

As our financial situation worsened week by week, the quarrels between my parents became more bitter. My mother did not only accuse father for not providing for his family and being used by other people, but other matters were mentioned, of which I would have preferred to be left in ignorance. I was a coward. I did not want to hear about his gullibility, his irresponsible generosity to people he hardly knew and his affairs with women some time in the past.

One day mother shouted in exasperation: "And I am not so sure you are not having an affair with her, that strumpet. The way you talk to her, the way she looks at you."

My father contorted his face in disgust.

"And where were you yesterday afternoon? Tell me that. You left half an hour after she did."

"Oh, don't be silly, Sarah − child. I wouldn't touch her for all the gold in the world."

My mother had to laugh. "For all the gold in the world," she said, "well . . . I don't know. In that case I might want to persuade you."

They came together and kissed. They were close. I glowed.

I went for many walks. There was not much secretarial work to do for my father. The flat was cramped, the atmosphere often tense and it was best to get away.

There was the famous Spielberg ('Play Mountain') with the infamous castle where a number of cruelties had taken place according to the historical accounts. I never went into it.

I found my own secret places amongst the dense trees and thick bushes. I avoided other people. I lived a kind of double life.

Of course I was deeply involved and immediately affected by what was going on at home. The parents difficulties were also mine. My relationship with them was not close in the usual sense. But even in those days I was aware of the unseen

49

chains which linked us all together. Paul too was part of it, of course, although he lived away from us. I prayed constantly for a way out. But I knew that none of us would want to separate himself voluntarily.

Those walks. Now I could be my other self: the boy adoring God in the trees, in the sky. I, the young poet, wanted to have a dialogue with Him. I felt close to nature.

Even now I have not learnt the names of the trees and the wild plants and the common birds. I never found out how everything grows, multiplies, survives.

I was afraid of prickles and stings. To animals I could never relate. But life, any form of life, I treasured. Even as a small child I was sorry for every picked flower and every dead insect. If absentmindedly I tore off a leaf from a tree, I often returned it to the tree to which it had belonged.

I was isolated. I lived in a world which was difficult to share with anybody. I believed I was favoured. It was not necessary for me to learn much. Knowledge could only be a hindrance. I did not mind that my formal education had to be interrupted. I did not really want to learn. Learning was for others. Details did not concern me. I could reach my goal without particular skills. What was important for me was to write poetry.

I loved nature in my own way. Not its parts but its totality: the view, the smell, the sound. The touch of a few blades of grass was like an embrace of a whole meadow.

All was created for me.

> 'The ears of the corn
> are lowered
> as I pass by.'

My faith began to take shape. 'Good' can also mean 'painful' or 'unbearable' or even 'tragic'. Whatever was to happen to me would be 'right' for me, even if others would think it 'wrong'. I may not be able to see it at the time. Only later, much later, years later, I might be permitted — as a special privilege — to understand the pattern of the roads I had walked on. I will perceive then, that I could not have gone any other way.

Nothing as yet was formalised. The belief gained strength later, particularly during our pilgrimage through Poland. But the seeds had been sown. How could I have written this, if I had been without faith?

> 'Show yourself Lord
> Your decision
> Is always sound
> It will happen as
> As you will
>
> But
> Show yourself
> Show
> Your decision.'

Even Martin had some difficulty at times finding his hideouts again. There was one where he had to leave the main path, where two hedges tried without success to touch each other in the breeze. The gap was wide enough for Martin to slip through. Then he passed more bushes and trees, nodding to them and after a while was welcomed by two outstretched leafy branches. The slight wind raised the grass, the bushes shivered and the heads of the wild flowers were bent.

Martin did not have a very good sense of direction. But here he knew his way. Human voices and human noises he had left behind. Winding himself through the jungle of shrub-like plants, he got to a small clearing, just roomy enough for him to settle down and stretch out. Looking up there were tiny patches of blue, ever-changing. Clouds were hastily swept away. The trees were very tall in this place. But there was enough light to keep out fear. This was one of Martin's temples. Here he felt at peace.

He took from his pockets letters from Paul, from Georg, from Toni and read them again. He almost knew them by heart. He took comfort from what Paul had written, smiled about the letter from Toni which was in the form of a dialogue and a page sent by Georg he put to his lips.

51

Then he sat very still for a while. Later he found a pencil in his jacket and started to write on the back of an envelope:

'What are you doing, strange boy?
I am touching the trees, my God.
What are you doing, strange boy?
I kiss the leaves of the bushes, my God,
They are so soft.
What are you doing, strange boy?
I loosen my clothes, my God.
They fall away like chains of iron.
What are you doing, strange boy?
I am bathing, I am bathing,
I am bathing in you.
What are you doing, strange boy?
I am living, my God, I am living.'

Martin stood up. His hand shook holding the envelope. "A new poem by Martin Forest," he called out and then he read it aloud. He remained silent as if waiting for a response. After a while he undressed and lay down.

He had an orgasm.

We left Fräulein Beova's flat shortly after the Munich crisis, I don't know why. Perhaps the parents thought it best to move because of Fräulein's advances towards me. Once she had involved me in some doubtful conversation in the kitchen with the blankets still ruffled on the camp-bed. She had asked me whether I had a girlfriend and if I did not think it was high time that I learnt 'what is what' in practice. It puzzles me now why I should have mentioned it to the parents. Maybe I wanted to demonstrate to them that there was at least one person who took an interest in me. But it is more likely that I wanted to cause annoyance. My father was amused, my mother was furious. She walked out of the room into the kitchen and told Fräulein Beova that there was in Breslau a very pretty girl with long black hair, only waiting for her emigration papers in order to join me. This was a complete fabrication. There was no girl waiting for me anywhere. Soon afterwards we packed our cases once again. There was now very little money left from the jewellery which had been sold eighteen months ago. There was no income. Because of the German occupation of the Sudetenland, Czech firms were even less inclined than before to expand their export trade. We had become very poor.

The tiny rooms were changed for a roomy 'apartment' with the Novaks on the other side of the town, an industrial district. You opened the green wooden gate in the street by lifting up the latch. The sweet smell of warm sausage meat greeted you (Herr Novak was a butcher). Then you climbed some narrow steps to the second floor of the house. The door opened to the kitchen. The two rooms leading from it were very large and quite adequately furnished. There was, of course, no grand piano here, no comfortable leather armchairs and the wallpaper was unattractive. Certainly if you compared this flat with the one we had had in Germany, we now lived in a hovel. But my mother did not grumble. Now she had her own kitchen.

The Novaks were not only sympathetic to our plight, they expressed their dislike of the Nazis in no uncertain terms. They let us live our lives without interfering.

We got very depressed for various reasons. But my parents did not quarrel so much. Perhaps they had a premonition that some unavoidable disaster was going to affect us soon. There was less friction now. We did not tear each other to pieces any more.

Both Paul and I learnt a new trade. I have already told you how this experience threw me into the depth of despair. We saw less and less of Paul. The journey from Prague to Brünn was expensive. My father left the flat every morning "to see some people with influence who could perhaps help." He made appointments with members of the Lodge to which he had belonged in Germany. Brothers of the Lodge were supposed to be always prepared to assist each other. I think he was given both advice and promises but no cash. And it was cash we were short of. Even father could not conceal his bitterness. The various suggestions by the Brothers were quite impracticable and could not be taken seriously.

The day came when we had no more money. It was time to register with the local Refugee Centre and ask for financial help. I was too deeply involved in my own affairs to realise what this must have meant to my father. Until now he had never been able to face matters. An unsuccessful dreamer, an easy match for anyone wanting to take advantage of his unquestioning naivety, an introvert, sensitive, aware of his inadequacy, a proud man who wanted to prove to his family that he was not a failure after all, he had to admit now to us and to himself, that it was necessary to ask for help from the welfare organisation. He had had such hopes, such plans, such grand designs for the future. Now he had to ask for charity. Of course, he deceived himself.

"I shall return every krone I get from them, Sarah — child," he stated more than once, "this is only an embarrassing emergency."

I accompanied him on several occasions after the carpentry course had folded, on his weekly trips to the refugee offices.

The key person there was Herr Schwarz, the official behind the counter. He was detestable: such a frail and insignificant looking man who wore a 'Käpl' on his head so that he would not stand naked before his God — and his clients who shivered in front of him. His voice was hardly audible but biting. He asked the most searching questions. How had the money been spent which had been handed out the previous week? What efforts had been made to obtain visas to Nicaragua? What about our relatives overseas? Could they not help? And the nephew in London? Had we heard from him? Why was one son in Prague? Would it not be cheaper for him to live with the rest of the family here in Brünn?

When my father replied, the little man shook his head every so often in apparent disbelief. Finally he wrote out a chit and father had to queue up downstairs and when he put the notes into his pocket the expression on his face was dark and his shoulders drooped. But as soon as we left the building, he straightened up.

"I shall pay back every krone with interest," he said, "I don't want to keep anything they give me."

While walking he said; "Actually, there is still some money

54

left, but nobody knows about it. Even your mother does not know. I have an idea. I can't talk about it yet. I shall need the money for that. But don't say anything to mother about it. And then there is the small amount you gave me, the money you had collected."

I did not reply. It was all such nonsense.

"I am just going into the town," my father said. "There is something I should like to do. You go along home. Tell mother I shall be in for lunch."

The betting shop was in the shopping arcade in the centre of the town.

A few weeks later Herr Schwarz directed that we should get out midday meals from the welfare kitchen. My mother walked now every day to the Refugee Centre with a couple of empty pots hidden away in the large leatherette shopping bag. She did not appear to mind all that much and in her usual way made friends with the woman who dished out the food. Our portions were rather generous. The food was warmed up at home and with a little modification and some spices, it was certainly edible. We behaved as if my mother had cooked it herself. The soup or the stew or the rice (with chocolate sauce) were shared out in the kitchen, the plates were brought into the room where the table was laid as usual.

Once I saw my father crying as he watched from the window, my mother in a simple green dress ("One must always dress according to the situation," she had said), walking quickly to our house with the pots concealed in the bag. My heart went out to her. I ran down the steps to assist her. But she was determined to carry this load herself.

One morning my cousin Willi arrived from nowhere. We had not seen him since we had left Breslau. We had heard some stories about the way he lived. But we did not believe them. Suddenly he was here, with us. He was penniless and hoped he could get something from us to tide him over.

"Can I stay for lunch?" he asked my mother, "I am sure, Aunt, your cooking is as good as it always was."

55

This was silly flattery. He had never tasted my mother's cooking. It was always a servant who cooked in Breslau until the last year or so, after Elsie left and mother was without any help in the kitchen.

"Of course you can stay for lunch," my mother said. She was too proud to admit that we got our meals from the welfare kitchen.

Looking back, the situation was comical. We had to keep Willi in ignorance of our predicament.

My father took me aside and whispered: "Take Willi for a walk, while mother goes to get the food."

I suggested to Willi a walk into town and this suited him as he had to go somewhere with a message.

We passed a club with a doubtful reputation. I had walked by it very often, wondering what was going on inside. Now in day time, the front looked seedy rather than glamorous. There were no beckoning neon lights.

"I won't be long," Willi said to me and disappeared through a side door. I waited outside furtively, throwing glances in all directions in case I should see someone I knew. But this was unlikely. Then Willi stood next to me, heaving a sigh of relief.

"At least I have got my watch back," he said to me, "but please don't mention anything to Uncle or Aunt."

He praised our midday meal. (We had smaller portions than usual.)

"Of course, I knew I would eat well here," he said.

My father gave him a few kronen, which we could ill afford. Willi said he would make his way to Prague somehow.

A few months later I met Willi again in Kattowitz. He asked me to take over the clerical work for the Refugee Committee. Shortly after we had arrived there, he was to travel to England.

*　　*　　*　　*

Willi never knew what an important part he played in my childhood. We had never been close. He was not really my cousin. His mother and mine, although related, were not sisters. The elderly Aunt Minna, who came to visit either

56

us or the Lindens every other week, was not a genuine aunt either. But Aunt Minna and the Lindens were the only relatives my mother had, apart from grandfather, of course, who lived with us. Aunt Minna was one of the ladies who took over the care of my mother, then a teenager, when her mother died. It was all very complicated. I never bothered to find out what these family relationships on my mother's side were.

Herr and Frau Linden I called 'uncle' and 'aunt'. Their children, Anton, Susanna and Willi were my 'cousins'. The white haired, grey-clothed lady who often came unannounced into our home, talking to us as if she had grit between her teeth, always grudging and grumbling, she was 'Aunt Minna'.

I was always jealous of the Lindens. I overheard mother telling Paul once, that Aunt and Uncle Linden were still in love with each other, after all these years. Everyone knew this had been a love match. There was never a rumour that Herr Linden was unfaithful to his wife. No other woman existed for him.

"In spite of her unshapely legs," my mother said. She was proud of hers.

"The Lindens are well off, have always been well off," my father said, "he has inherited property and capital from his father. And then there is the family business, established for decades."

"The Linden children are the best children in the world," said Aunt Minna looking at me with some distaste, "they are all handsome and clever."

Susanna wanted to become a nurse, Anton won many prizes in athletics, and Willi . . . "Well, we all know Willi: good at school, the best son parents could wish for, and always obedient, considerate, such a kind child and helpful to his Aunt Minna," said Aunt Minna.

How I envied the Lindens.

Their flat was a walking distance from ours in Breslau. But they had a garden. There was the scent of flowers. And a swing. They spoke quietly to each other. They respected each other. Nobody seemed to be cross with anybody. Aunt Linden always seemed happy to see me when I went to visit them. On one occasion she made me an unexpected present: a fountain pen with a red top.

I envied the Lindens. Particularly I envied Willi. What must it be like to be a member of such a family!

The Lindens possessed a weekend house at the foot of the Zobten Mountain. The Zobten, a spur of the Silesian Giant mountains was only a short journey away from Breslau by slow train. It looked grand from below, stretching over 700 metres into the sky. It was covered with trees, saplings and shrubs, except the top. Up there stood a little church and from its tower one could see, on clear days, the whole of Silesia. (Sometimes after the rain when the air was clean, I could make out the outlines of the mountain from the window of the servants' room at home.) How much I wanted to live there. Just to wake up in the mornings, to smell the strong fresh aroma of the mountains, to run into the woods and listen to its sounds. Willi could. His family went to their villa nearly every week. They played table-tennis on the covered terrace, or worked in the garden, or climbed the mountain or went for walks.

Aunt Minna reported to us that she had seen Willi clearing a large patch of stones, carrying away heavy pieces of rock in his small wheel barrow. (How he had enjoyed the hard work.)

On top of the mountain there were indeed many rocks of all sizes. One could jump from one to another. Or play hide-and-seek. Or get lost amongst them.

How I envied Willi. No wonder he was such a good child, good at his lessons, good to his parents, good to Aunt Minna. Wouldn't I be, if I could lead his kind of life?

Willi's friends were not mine, we had different interests. But once, on a tram journey, coming home from school, he told me about the summer holiday, which he had spent with his parents, his brother and his sister by the Baltic Sea.

"Early one morning," he said, "when the others were still asleep, I got up and dressed and walked very slowly along the beach. There was nobody else around. I was the only one. The only sound was the breaking of the waves."

At that moment I felt I was related to him. Although I had been to the sea before when I was a toddler, I had no memories of it. Hearing Willi talking, I felt as he must have felt.

When I met Willi in Brünn, I reminded him of what he had told me many years previously. He said that the family had been to the Baltic Sea once, but he could not remember any details of this holiday.

One Sunday afternoon when Aunt Minna had come to see us, she told my mother about Willi's success in the recent arithmetic test. "Of course," she said, "Willi's mark is 'very good' — as usual." Glancing at me, she asked with a hint of malice in her voice; "And Martin? How did Martin do?"

The teacher's comment had been 'barely satisfactory'. That sort of grade was not unexpected.

Mother turned to me with an angry flushed face: "So you lied to me," she cried out, "you told me that Willi's mark was lower than yours."

"So it was," I said, convinced for once that I was in the right.

"Martin, you bring shame on your parents," Aunt Minna butted in, "you should always tell the truth. I know you are lying because I spoke to Willi's mother only yesterday."

"Willi couldn't do his sums," I whined, "he got a lot of them wrong."

"We shall soon see," threatened my mother and lifted up the receiver of the telephone.

I was sent to my room to await the outcome of the telephone conversation and possible judgement. It turned out that Aunt Minna had misunderstood what she had been told, the mark 'very good' had referred to last year's general performance at school. (Mine had been: 'barely satisfactory'.) To everyone's amazement, Willi had kept to himself the result of this particular arithmetic test. Even Aunt Minna agreed that he had behaved in a 'deceitful manner'. His parents were shocked. He was not allowed to go to Zobten the following weekend. He went to stay with Aunt Minna instead.

Willi did not speak to me for some time afterwards. Aunt Minna also did not visit us for a few weeks. My mother had kissed me: "I should not have called you a liar. But you know, as I do, that at times you don't tell the truth."

My poor Aunt Minna. She must have been a very unhappy

woman to bring so much gloom into our home. She did not like any of us, not even my grandfather who was closest to her. Perhaps she did not care for us, because we never cared for her.

One day she had a stroke. There she lay on her pillow, paralysed and without speech, unable to make her wishes known. She could not even complain of the Rosens any more.

When I had to go to the funeral service at the crematorium, I was afraid I would have to see the burning of her coffin. There were some holes covered with glass sunk into the wall of the small temple. I had been told, if one wanted, one could look through and see the coffin disappearing in a sea of flames. Perhaps it was only a show laid on for the mourners. But I turned away after the service and went outside. The sun was shining. I was thinking back: Did Aunt Minna ever say anything nice about me? Once. Yes. Once she had said to my grandfather when I had shown some concern for somebody: "Martin is kind-hearted. He may not be very clever, but he is kind-hearted."

Aunt Minna was spared the knowledge of the misfortunes of the Linden family. We did not know then of Willi's instability.

Not long after Aunt Minna's death, Anton, the sportsman, whom I had seen only rarely and usually on the sportsfield, came to us to say 'good-bye'. He was on the way to Argentina. His parents were against the idea of such a sudden emigration, but Anton had made up his mind. He wanted to become a farmer. There was still time to leave Germany. He begged his parents to come with him. They were convinced, as were so many Jewish families at that time, that Hitler would soon lose his power. Then his sister Susanna completed her training in nursing and was soon working in a hospital in London. After the sale of the Zobten weekend house, the Lindens decided to go to Mexico, where Herr Linden had business contacts. Hitler was not going to stay for long, but the opportunity was unique and had to be taken. Willi was to complete his school education, live with friends and join the parents in the following year. There was also some property in the process of being sold. This additional capital was essential for the building up of the new business in Mexico. Jewellery and expensive cameras would be purchased for Willi to take abroad. Everything had been planned in detail.

What happened to all these possessions after Willi left Germany, I don't know. We heard later that his parents never received any of the proceeds. Willi never mentioned anything when we met him in Brünn. Uncle Linden was not very successful in Mexico, but made some kind of living. No doubt, his wife continued to adore him. During the war he had a heart attack and died. Whether Willi kept in touch with his parents, I don't know. Anton, after years of very hard work on the land, bought his own farm, married a chubby, healthy-looking Argentinian girl and fathered many children who looked like organ pipes on the photograph which somebody showed me years ago. Aunt Linden could not live without her husband. She jumped out of the window from her flat on the seventh floor. Susanna became depressed in London, she had an unhappy love affair and took an overdose. (My mother went to her funeral, nobody attended but a young man in a dark suit.) Willi married a charming, pretty girl. Paul and I were invited to tea to meet her. Willi had become a waiter in one of Lyons Corner Houses. Not much later we heard that he had left her. I was told by someone who knew him, that Willi was now in Switzerland.

How jealous I had been of the family Linden.

My poor Aunt Minna. If she only knew.

*   *   *   *

As we had feared, the march of the Germans into the Sudetenland had only been the prelude to the complete occupation of Czechoslovakia.

One day in March 1939, the swastikas were flying from the roofs of the houses in our street. Loudspeakers announced Hitler's arrival. He made a speech in the same square where, only two years earlier, the people had stood with lowered heads, mourning for Masaryk.

The Novaks behaved exemplarily. In spite of the Czech

61

name, they were of German extraction. But they assured us (Frau Novak had tears in her eyes) that they would never throw us out even if ordered to do so. From time to time they sent meat upstairs to us.

We lived in fear. True, we did not see hordes of brown-shirts in the streets and after a few weeks we did not expect to be fetched and transported to a camp. But what would the future hold for us? We had no immediate opportunity to emigrate, we were poor and there was the constant uncertainty of possible action by the Nazis against German Jewish refugees.

I had time on my hands. My walks became explorations. I visited some of the churches in the town, the monastery and the palace, and then went further: to the field at Austerlitz where the historical battle had taken place.

When the guide informed us about the 'outstanding strategic victory of Napoleon'; I looked across the fields where thousands of young men had lost their lives or had suffered. I asked the guide:

"Do you think there is anything worth the killing and maiming of people?"

He replied: "That depends on the cause."

I regretted my impetuosity. This was German-occupied country. Somebody could have taken notice of what I had said.

For weeks I lived in fear that I had been reported to the Nazis. The Gestapo would not find it very difficult to get hold of our address. They would come and take me away.

The fear of possible consequences of my actions has never left me. Whom have I harmed by what I have done?

Did a letter which I wrote cause unhappiness or illness or even death?

Was the present I had accepted stolen property?

What could happen to me?

Would my parents be affected by the wrong information I gave unwittingly on a questionnaire?

I played my own game of consequences. I thought through all the possible steps which would have to be taken or the possible sequence of events which had to occur, before finally the blame could be laid on me. There were always too many steps, discovery was therefore unlikely. That was all right as long as the consequences could have repercussions only on me. I could carry them. I was prepared to accept punishment.

But what about other people I meet, however fleetingly? There is no encounter, however trivial, which does not leave some trace. We all affect each other, I knew. There are consequences to all our meetings.

Living seemed to be too complicated at times.

A memory of an outing makes me feel as if I am losing my balance, as if the boat might topple over at any moment. Life was precarious in those days.

Frau Binder's insane son had mentioned the grottos. I had never seen stalagmites and stalactites. It was not the season for visiting grottos. I joined a small group.

Walking together through the underground church with its fantastic spires, altars and sculptures, we became close, almost intimate, in our adorations.

Suddenly someone shouted from another cave.

We were ordered to halt and after a few minutes, a high-ranking SS man adorned with medals on his black coat and another uniformed man joined us. I wanted to get away. I looked round to see whether there was an exit sign. I was in a panic but tried not to show it. But a woman must have observed me. She turned her head towards me and asked: "Are you all right, young man?"

I pretended I had slipped on the wet slimy limestone ground.

There was no way out for me.

The Germans only spoke to each other.

The guide invited us to climb into one of the two little boats which had been fastened to the bank of the underground river.

I nearly fell into the water.

The two uniformed men sat opposite me.

They looked at me. They peered at me.

Had they noticed my nervousness?

Did my face show that I was a Jew?

At any moment they would ask for my name.

Rosen.

Rosen. A Jewish name.

They would lean over me, get hold of me and throw me into the ice cold water.

And leave me to struggle.

Terror within me: my heart was racing.

But the Nazis were on their best behaviour. No doubt they wanted to impress the Czechs. I prayed they would not arrest me once we were outside the caves. As soon as there was light, I walked away quickly. I felt very sick.

We were hopeful. At least Kattowitz was something tangible to aim for. The illegal crossing of the border, out of sight of both Czech and Polish frontier police was, we understood, child's play. Neither the Czechs who would be only too willing to deceive the Germans, nor the Poles, would make any difficulties. But we needed a guide. A guide who knew that part of the country. A guide who could be trusted.

I cannot remember who recommended him. He came to our flat one evening to brief us. We parted with the little money we still had. Father produced the few notes he had tucked away. The day was fixed. The second Sunday in May. We were to take the train to Moravska Ostrava. Fitted out like hikers with raincoats and rucksacks. We were going to attend a Sunday Service in a little chapel near the border. Then a leisurely stroll and soon we would find ourselves in Poland. It was up to us to make our own way to Kattowitz. It was all very easy. Nothing to worry about. There were many people who had crossed the border the same way. All had succeeded. The Czechs were not interested. The Poles were usually lethargic, particularly before lunch on a Sunday. In any case, they could not care less, the guide assured us, whether a few more refugees entered the country on their way to another. They knew Poland was only meant as a temporary stay.

"See you outside the station in Moravska Ostrava," he said, putting away the notes into his wallet.

We trusted him.

64

In the meantime we behaved normally. I continued going for my walks. My mother fetched the meals from the welfare kitchen and my father lay bets with the few kronen which he occasionally found in the pockets of his trousers. Paul stayed in Prague.

For some time I had attended classes in English held by the Berlitz School. These classes should not be missed, my parents advised. But there was no class on Friday before the fateful Sunday. The doors of the school were bolted.

I sat outside on the steps. There was no hurry to get home. There never was any hurry. Around me it was still. It was early evening, the houses stood in shadow. A few cars rushed by. When their noise ebbed away, all was quietness.

'This is a way of saying 'good-bye',' I thought.

I had loved the town. I had loved the pain I had felt. Two years of pain. But there was something sweet about that pain which held me as if to say: 'Well, are you stronger now?' The pain belonged to me, to me, Martin. My anger, my disappointments, my despairs: all these were mine. They belonged to me, they had nothing to do with anyone else. And these lonely walks were also mine, like the poems I had written. 'All these are mine', I thought and I was almost jubilant. I thought 'I have had a glimpse into some truth. Nothing exists unless you make it exist.'

But then I shook my head. I could not understand my own thoughts.

"Why are you shaking your head?" I heard a woman's voice, deep, musical.

"Oh, I was just thinking. And thinking became too complex," I replied. I knew her. She attended the same English classes. I had never spoken to her before. She was different from the other students. She was older, more mature. I had always been impressed by the way she was dressed. 'With taste', I thought. I was trying to guess her age. Twenty-five? Twenty-eight?

"No class?" she asked.

"Nobody here," I replied, "no point waiting. I am just taking a rest before going back home."

65

"They must have announced last week — that there would be no class."

"Neither of us have paid any attention," I joked and was surprised how freely I could talk to her.

"Come, take me home and have coffee with me," she said.

"I would love a cup of coffee," I replied.

She lived in comfort. The furniture was new. The armchairs and the settee were modern, in bright colours. There were lots of cushions. There was a large woollen off-white carpet. I remember the reproductions. Dutch interiors. Anyhow, I thought they were Dutch interiors. It is odd that I can remember furnishing so well. Of course, it is true I always craved comfort and luxury. But here was a woman who had invited me into her home. It would have been more important to remember what she looked like. But I cannot really visualise her any more. She was petite. And well groomed. Her face was delicately carved. Her fingernails carefully manicured. But this is all. I cannot recall her features. Her voice I can call up. I can still breathe in her scent of some unknown oriental fruit. (Like mandarins, but more mellow with just a hint of cinnamon.) I have repeated our conversation outside the language school, almost word for word. But I don't know what we talked about over coffee. But I remember she told me that she was married and that her husband was away in Prague.

I had settled down on the settee and then I saw her rise from the armchair, in slow motion almost, and come over to me. She sat beside me. I did not touch her. You will understand that I would have not dared to do so. She held my hand for a while. She embraced me. And she kissed me. Me, me. You understand, she kissed me, on the mouth, on my lips, in spite of my lip, or because of it, I don't know. She did not mind. She did not mind my ugliness. She kissed me and I responded. I could respond to her. No woman has ever kissed me again like this, no woman.

They were not only sensual kisses. There was also tenderness. And passion. It was as if we disclosed something of ourselves to each other. She made me reveal something of myself which I had always kept to myself. When we afterwards undressed and made love, of course she had to be my

66

teacher.

She filled us both with some inner knowledge, an understanding which went far beyond our mutual need for physical satisfaction.

When I left her, everything looked different, smelt different and felt different. But I felt no pride because of my achievement, as you might expect a boy to feel after his first sexual encounter. Something had come to an end, I knew it.

My closeness with her was like a full stop.

How grateful I was for this unexpected, glorious get-together. And yet I knew it was also a sign of farewell.

Not only would we never meet again. The day after tomorrow the family would leave this town, a town, which, so I thought, I had created myself, created with all my senses.

Something had been completed.

Was it really the end of my childhood? And would I now, the man Martin, be different from the boy Martin?

I knew that the Martin within me would remain the same.

* * * *

Extracts from letters to Martin, February 1938—April 1938, Breslau/Prague:

From Georg:

Your letter affected me very much. It touched me deeply, not so much with what you tell me, but beyond the written word, with the look into your inner-self which once again you have opened for me.

From Georg:

I am worried about you. You are in danger of drowning. You are not standing on firm ground. You must at last become clear about yourself. We are both old enough to find our balance. Certainly, you are gifted, but you can only use your gift properly after you have found yourself. Talent can only bear fruit when it is well embedded in the artist. Then the breakthrough will come eventually. But with you everything is so frail, so delicate. Like a spider's web you will be torn to pieces, should there be a storm.

Martin, you have so much more to give than the people around you. Why should you suffer amongst them? For heaven's sake, compose yourself, examine your abilities and attainments and face people with more strength.

Oh, I know how beautiful suffering can be, but I also know about its dangers.

From Toni:

You: How do you do. It's high time you come to see me again.

I: Hello, Martin. We are meeting on the first day of spring. It seems a long time ago when we talked to each other. First of all, I must tell you about the most wonderful surprise you gave me. Your poems. I read them through and I was quite composed. But then, I could not help myself, I shouted, I was so filled with enthusiasm.

You: Well, don't exaggerate.

I: As you know, I don't find it easy to express in words how I feel. But your poems gave me a lot.

You: I am glad you told me. One does not write poems merely for oneself.

From Paul:

Your beautiful poem shows that you have not altogether lost your inner strength. I feel empty and tired.

Yes, you are right, we all have to carry the fate of Ahasveros, an important but horrible fate of a people who are not allowed to die out.

From Paul:

Here is the same as in Brünn. I am suspended between hope and disappointment. The swing of the pendulum is becoming less. There are fewer hopes and therefore also fewer disappointments.

Once again you have the more difficult share. Who can explain this?

From Georg:

I have also felt during the last days the split between my parents and myself. But my case is different from yours. What I wanted, you find difficult and painful. You must also understand that it can't be easy for your mother. Don't take me wrong. I don't mean that you are a 'difficult' child. But you are strange, not like others. Of course, you are right, when you demand from your parents that they get to know their children. But you must forgive them if they are not prepared to do so. And you may be wrong, you know. Perhaps they *are* trying. But you are so impatient and excited, you rip open old wounds and you are torturing both your mother and yourself. How pointless all this is. And instead of recovery and peace, you continue to suffer. How can you lose all control and talk about your poems to your mother, expecting to bring about a change in her attitude to you? The way your mother responded is difficult to forgive, I know, and I could weep, suffering with you.

One thing I am sure about. You must be wrong when you write that your brother has 'withdrawn' from you. You do him wrong when you doubt his love for you. Of course, it is quite possible that he condemns or criticises certain things about you. He may well be justified.

From Toni:

When I come home in the evening and find letters from Berlin, Cologne, Frankfurt, Hamburg and Brünn on the table, then I am as happy as anyone can be. And when I open the letter from Brünn and start to read it, then with each word one kilometre disappears and it does not take long before we are physically close to each other. Then the letter becomes conversation. When I have finished reading, I know that you wrote as you felt. Well you should know by now how dear you are to me.

From Georg:

I don't know what your thoughts are on your birthday, but perhaps you are experiencing it as I do: the past life like a dream, both a bad dream and a smiling one. We look around. We reach back.

69

Yes, a dream. We have been without will or strength. We suffered what was joyful and what was painful, just as it happened. But don't shed tears over it, don't mourn for it. In front of you the road lies open and bright. From the dream into life, the beautiful colourful life which we must always mould, awake, not dreaming. The future will become past again, but don't think of it. If you do, everything is illusion and there is no truth.

I can't send you a book for your birthday as this is not permitted by the authorities. But to give you a book would be without meaning in our relationship. In your last letter you said that poems are revelations. I am enclosing a few small drawings which I did for you. These are my revelations.

From Paul:

I am making use of a quiet hour to write to you to let you know how much I feel for you.

The days are spent in coming face to face with the national consciousness of a people. I happened to be in the Wenzel Square when the last governmental manifesto was read out and the people stood with lowered heads and wept.

What will happen now, no one knows. September 1938 will be a month to remember. It is quite pointless to make serious plans. One has got to make the right decisions at the right time.

I must tell you about a night I shall not forget. For a whole night I was under the impression that war had broken out and that an air-raid was imminent. During the night when the Czechs mobilised, I heard voices in the street, shouts to turn the lights off. I saw Prague from my window in complete darkness. Then I knocked at the door of my landlady and tried to find out what had happened in my very halting Czech. She said "There is war". It is not possible to describe my feelings during the long sleepless hours, but it is only fair to say, that fear was not foremost. I packed my suitcase next morning and ran to the news stand only to find out that it was not as bad as all that.

From Paul:

You won't believe how much I envy you your work in

70

spite of your complaints and doubts. First of all you are occupied during the day and very tired in the evening as you always wanted to be. Then, I assure you, what you regard as a lack in aptitude is mainly the novelty. I am convinced that you will perform sufficiently well as a carpenter, although you may not reach excellence. And it is so important to be skilled in something different later. They laughed at me when I told them I was a medical student and I can only hope that the courses begin here in Prague soon, so that I can provide myself with a 'vocational cloak'. I don't expect to get a complete training, neither must you. Well, chin up and remember:

> 'Hans Sachs, he made a shoe
> He was a poet too . . . '

From Toni:

Never in the past did I suspect that I, the wretched little scout, meant so much to you, and I can't help feeling a little proud. But you are making a mistake when you say you in turn could not give me anything. Neither do I wish to flatter you nor have I got the time to do so. But I do hope that you are aware of your own personal qualities.

From Paul:

I am referring to your Palestinian plan. If one only knew whether there is still enough time to stay here and use it to learn something (at present I am hoping to get on a course in welding). This would be preferable to a trip into the blue, although I understand that not only recruitment into the Police and the Army is possible, but also entry into the settlements. I know that you and I fear to let go chances which may never occur again, but I beg you to find out the precise date of the transport and whether there is another one in the future.

Otherwise there is nothing to tell. I need not tell you about my frame of mind. Physically I am very well – I am almost ashamed to admit it.

From Paul:

I have started a course in electrical engineering, at present

71

only theory (no difficulty for the 'medical man'). The afternoons I spend mostly in the library. I like the friendly peace there. When people are reading they can be tolerated.

The winter of discontent will soon be gone. Today we had snow but it is already melting.

From Georg:
I can't put it into words how grateful I am that you once again sent me your poems. It pains me not to be able to see you, not to be able to look into your eyes. But believe me, since the beginning of our friendship, my good wishes for you have never been as intense as now, when we live so far away from each other.

II

TRANSITS

Sunday was a sunny May day. The family Rosen was excited. In the afternoon they would be with their relatives in Kattowitz. They were expected. Martin who had loved Brünn in spite of or because of the two past difficult years so full of anguish, which he had expressed in his poetry, was now happy that this particular episode in his life was coming to a close. In front of him was a new life. He was looking forward to it.

His parents too were hopeful once more. Everything had been so full of disappointments. Matters could only improve. Of course, it may take a little time to get to London, but one had waited for such a long time, a month or two wait in Kattowitz would not make any difference. The Nazis would be on the other side of the frontier. One would be able to live without the constant feeling of insecurity.

Herr Rosen was full of plans, of course. Once in England, it was surely possible to start exporting some goods. It would not prove too difficult to find manufacturers who would be interested. South America was known to be interested in the development of such a trade.

Frau Rosen had no illusions about the future. Her husband, she knew, lacked both circumspection and vision. It was no use relying on his schemes. But there were other members of the family in London. She did not trust them, it is true, but they would not let the Rosens starve. It would look too bad if they did. The good opinions of others

73

mattered a great deal to them. And then there were one or two friends who had emigrated from Germany and lived now in London. She would not be on her own any more. There would always be someone to talk to. 'And I won't have to fetch lunches from the soup kitchen,' she thought.

Only Paul was saddened. He had left behind in Prague people he had been very fond of. And he had loved, loved so much, Rita. If he could have stayed, their physical relationship would have improved perhaps. And it had been sufficient to be near her physically, even if making love was difficult for some reason and disappointing. Rita planned to come to London, but would she really want to see him again? Would she not, perhaps, find someone else, someone stronger and simpler?

The brothers sat next to each other in the compartment. The parents were in another part of the train. The guide had stressed that they should not draw attention to themselves but behave like people on a Sunday afternoon outing.

"There are always people about," he had said, "who for a little reward are only too happy to give information to the Nazis. If only to save their own skins, sometimes. Particularly now, as things stand in this country. Behave normally in the train. No serious talk. And no politics."

Paul and Martin found it difficult to make conversation. Too much had happened and was happening, to be able to make small talk. For much of the journey they were silent.

Paul wondered whether he would be given the opportunity to continue his medical studies in England. But he was not sure whether he wanted to become a physician. Was the human body really an object one could devote one's life to? The mind, Paul thought, that was a different matter. Psychiatry, that would be an interesting study. 'Perhaps, I should aim to become a psychiatrist,' Paul thought.

Martin tried to relive the miraculous encounter with the young woman. But it seemed to him now that it had not really happened. Looking out of the window, he played the train games as he had played them when he was a child. A game with the telegraph poles, guessing the distance

74

between each by counting. And then: hoping that on just one occasion the ever-lowering wires would not spring up, suddenly, as if stung and return to their original height.

Then he noticed a fat man who sat a fair distance away from him, looking at them. There was no doubt, he was observing them. The man's eyes rested on the rucksacks which the brothers held on their thighs. At first Martin pretended that he was not aware of the man's interest in them, but then he looked straight into the man's face, daring him to say something, to shout out accusations. But the man said nothing. Martin wanted to alert Paul, but he did not wish to arouse more suspicion. 'I am probably imagining it,' he thought, 'but then, perhaps all this has been arranged. Maybe the guide has sold us out.' He tried to push away such thoughts. Was it really likely? What would be the consequences? If the man over there knew the real reason of this journey to Moravska Ostrava, what could he possibly do? Perhaps he was in league with the guide. But then they could have reported them to the Germans by now. They know of our flight. He was more likely to tell the Czech guard about them. And the Czech guard? Why should he wish to report them to the Nazis? There were no Germans about. Perhaps the Nazis already knew about them. 'Why should they delay arresting us? It is all rubbish."

"Nonsense," Martin said aloud.

"What is the matter?" asked Paul with a worried look.

"Oh, nothing," replied Martin, "I'm thinking nonsense."

"It's not a bad time to think nonsense. Serious matters are somehow out of place. Nothing can be more serious than our situation."

Martin threw Paul a warning glance.

"Yes, I know, it's a nice day for a long walk," said Paul and then recited:
"May is here
  the trees are breaking
  into leaf . . . "

"I hope it does not rain this afternoon. It would spoil everything."

"Indeed it would."

The train was steaming into the station. 'It's too noisy

75

for others to hear my racing heart,' thought Martin. Climbing down from the carriage, they heard the call from the parents. They were already on the platform. They recognised the guide who stood by the exit looking at a magazine. They pretended not to know him, as had been arranged.

"This is like a very bad film," said Paul quietly to Martin.

Martin said: "Where do we go from here?" It was hardly a question.

"You are the one who knows," said Paul and he sounded a little bitter.

"I never said I knew where I was going," replied Martin. "Somebody knows."

"As long as somebody does. Come along."

The parents had already passed through the barrier, following the guide. The brothers handed in their tickets and followed them. Martin thought: 'I have not seen him leaving the train. The fat man stayed in his seat. Another one of my groundless fears.' And then he remembered a children's book which he had read years ago, one of the few books he had enjoyed reading when he was a child. Kästners: *Emil and the Detectives*. What was the name of that crook, who had taken the notes of money pinned to the inside of Emil's jacket on the train to his grandmother in Berlin? Grindel? Grundel? Grundeis. Yes, Grundeis. But was it not Emil who followed the crook? 'Whom are we following?' Martin thought.

They had crossed the main road and now walked along a path by the side of a field. The guide led. Herr and Frau Rosen chatted to each other behind him. Between the parents and the brothers was a gap.

There was the little country church hidden by trees.

"What does one do in church?" asked Martin, "I have never been to a service in church."

"You do as everyone else does," said Paul, "you sit or stand and sometimes you kneel. You are even allowed to pray if you feel like it. Or you can recite poems to yourself. But knowing you, you probably don't know any. Apart from those you have written yourself."

"I know some nursery rhymes. And the first verses of folk-songs. What about this." Martin sang quietly:

"Now I leave, now I leave,

76

now I leave this little town,
leave this little town,
and you, my sweet, stay here."

For some reason the guide bypassed the church. This was against all that had been planned. The Rosens were to join the congregation, come out with the crowd and leave by a small gate at the back of the cemetery.

"I wonder why the guide has changed his mind," said Martin.

They went on. The figure of the guide seemed to get smaller and smaller.

"We shall soon have lost sight of him," said Paul.

At that moment two uniformed men suddenly appeared and marched briskly towards the parents. The boys did not stop but hurried on to catch up with the others.

As the parents could not speak Czech, Paul who knew some interpreted. Martin stood by, his eyes lowered, like a small boy who had been caught doing something naughty.

Paul explained. "They are Czech frontier guards. They want us to go with them to the border post."

"Tell them who we are," said Herr Rosen, "tell them that we are Jews running away from the Nazis."

Paul tried to explain that they were refugees, hated by the Germans and on their way to Kattowitz where relatives were waiting for them. One of the men nodded as if he fully understood the implications, the other shook his head in disbelief. Then they talked to Paul who tried to make sense of it.

"All this will be sorted out," Paul tried to sound encouraging, "they seem to realise our position."

Another guard had appeared in the meantime. The group walked across the field laden with buttercups. The men joked, but the family Rosen had nothing to say to each other. Frau Rosen clung to Paul, and Martin, walking next to his father, felt closer to him than he had for many years. Martin wondered what had happened to the guide who had seemed to be so trustworthy. But he did not ask his father. It was unimportant now.

At the border post — a large hut — there was an officer who spoke good German. Frau Rosen with her usual charm, tried to convince him that there was no question of attempting to smuggle anything across the border. The officer believed her. But this was not the issue. They were acting under orders. The family had tried to cross the frontier illegally. Their case was now being considered.

The Rosens ate the sandwiches prepared by Frau Rosen in Brünn. The little wooden partition where they sat on a bench resembled some place where hikers had taken shelter from the midday sun. A picnic lunch. Only Frau Rosen spoke to a young civilian official and tried to make him understand why the Jewish people were living in fear of the Nazis. The German-speaking officer returned. He said he hoped the family would soon be in England to start a new life. But some formalities had to be completed.

"You will have to go to Headquarters. Some paper work, you know. Back to the town. We shall take you in the car."

He spoke with great kindness. The Rosens smiled smiles of relief. Everything would be all right. They would let them go.

During the short journey back into the town, Herr Rosen comforted his wife.

"We shall soon be in Kattowitz, Sarah-child," he said.

Martin said to Paul: "I wonder whether they caught up with the guide?"

Paul replied: "Don't be so naive, Martin."

They drove through a residential area. Then the car stopped outside a rather imposing-looking residence. They were told not to get out.

Two tall SS men rushed to the car, opened the doors quickly. "Some more of these people," one of them said, disgust in his voice. "Get out and be quick about it," said the other.

'This is the stuff nightmares are made of,' thought Martin, as they were pushed along the path to the large door of the building.

They had arrived at the Gestapo Headquarters.

The Czechs had handed them over.

Once the home of a well-to-do family, the house had been requisitioned by the Germans after the occupation. Inside much was left as before: luxurious furniture and furnishing. Thick carpets. Brocade curtains. But the lower halves of the windows facing the street were covered with black cardboard. Pictures had been taken off, only the hooks remained. Posters of leading party men, charts and a map or two had been stuck on the walls.

Martin and Paul had to walk briskly along a passage through the house. The parents were behind them. Some of the doors they passed were slightly open. Rays of the afternoon sun had crept in as if lost. There was something obscene about the gentleness of this May Sunday which had found its way here.

'It makes no sense,' thought Martin, 'love and hate, both in one place.'

They had come to what must have once been a kitchen. The room was tiled, all the windows had been boarded up, the single bulb hanging from the ceiling threw a dim light.

Commands: "You lot, turn round and face the wall . . . no, you woman, don't join him. Stand over there. Face the wall. And you," — Paul was pushed — "you stand here, not there you idiot, now study the tiles in front of you. Silence. No talking. As soon as anyone opens his mouth, I shall see that it will remain closed for a very long time."

There the Rosens stood imprisoned in their thoughts. They lost the sense of time. They heard voices from somewhere in the belly of the building, rough and furious voices but also matter of fact voices, unconcerned. Now and again a scream or a whine.

They did not know whether there was anyone with them, guarding them. They expected to be beaten.

'Blood can easily be cleaned up here,' thought Paul.

But hours passed. They seemed to be ignored.

'Perhaps they are making arrangements for our transfer to a concentration camp,' thought Martin.

Then suddenly there was a heavy bump. Martin turned round instinctively. His eyes and those of Paul and father rested for just a moment on the crumpled heap on the floor.

A shout: "Eyes to the wall, you lot. This does not concern you."

Herr Rosen's small voice: "Can I help my wife?"

"You shut up. Don't you dare to move."

Silence. It was the first time that Martin noticed the ticking of the kitchen clock.

'What are they doing to her?' Paul thought.

A voice: "Sit there."

Somebody must have brought a chair for Frau Rosen.

"Thank you." It was Frau Rosen's almost soundless voice. "It is very kind of you."

Was it now evening? Or even night? Space and time had no meaning any more. The Rosens still faced the different walls. At least Frau Rosen was sitting. Steps could be heard from time to time coming nearer towards the kitchen. These were moments of terror. They were coming. They had decided what to do with them.

'There will be pain,' thought Martin.

'Shall I be able to bear it?' thought Paul.

And then, finally, there was action.

Herr Rosen was ordered out of the kitchen. The brothers heard the soft anxious sobbing of their mother.

After what seemed to be an endless time, someone returned.

'Father is back,' they thought.

Then it was Frau Rosen's turn. Then Paul's. Then Martin's.

Martin was following the SS man. 'What a big place this is,' he thought, and then: 'How ridiculous to think about the size of it.'

Outside a closed door, the man turned to him and spoke sharply: "You march in and stand inside the chalk circle in front of the desk. You will shout: 'I am the Jew Martin Rosen'. I shall be behind you, boy. If you don't shout loud enough, you soon will."

The door opened. Martin saw the circle clearly marked on the floor. He rushed to it, as if to seek shelter. But he stumbled and nearly fell. Perhaps it was the long time of standing which had weakened his legs.

"Stupid Jewish lout," the man shouted behind him, "can't you even lift your feet properly?"

Martin stood and swayed in the circle. A man in civilian clothes, looking like any man, sat behind the enormous leather covered desk. There was no aggression in his voice when he asked:

"Your name?"

"I am the Jew Martin Rosen," Martin shouted.

"No need to shout. I am not deaf . . . yet." And looking behind Martin he asked with irritation in his voice: "Why must you make these people shout out their names. It is pointless and annoys me." And to Martin: "You are the youngest of the family. Eighteen years old, correct?"

"Yes, Sir."

"You all want to get to England? You have relatives in England?"

"Yes Sir."

"We shall see. We shall see."

'I want to tell this man that I love him,' thought Martin.

"Turn round, march, left right, left, right."

Martin followed the SS man back into the kitchen. His father and Paul were still facing the wall. But his mother was not there any more. There was only an empty chair.

*　　*　　*　　*

There was a feeling of festivity when I woke up. What we had planned was actually going to happen. We were going to leave Brünn.

Nothing looked the same as yesterday. The room in which I had lived for so many months had been transformed. Is this really where I slept and dreamt and ate and wrote poems and thought? The bits of furniture, the shabby mat, the dull wallpaper: all this had become part of me, but now that I was to go away, it had separated itself already as if it wanted to exist without me.

Looking for the last time at the houses and the shops and the street corners and the trees flanking the roads, and the gardens in bloom, and the school without its bright noise, they entered into me and I hugged everything, but what I had loved had now become alien, remote. And these people, crowds of them, who did what they had done yesterday when they belonged to me, they are acting outside me. They do not know that I shall cross the border in a few hours, that

81

I shall be in a foreign country. They are part of a world which is mine no more. How depressing it would be, if it were not for the anticipation of change. The hope and the joy of being alive. Yes, the joy. And another aim. A further step towards fulfilment. No one can share the inner fever, the excitement within me, when the barriers are being opened for me to slip through and become part of something else.

Frau Novak wept and Herr Novak looked embarrassed, trying to hide his strong red butcher's hands when we said 'good-bye'. Although it was Sunday, the sweet odour of cooked sausage-meat still hung in the passage.

"Is it really necessary for you to go?" asked Herr Novak.

"You know you'll be safe with us," said Frau Novak.

"You will write to us from London," said Herr Novak.

They shook hands with Paul and me and then the latch of the gate to the street was lifted and we were on our way to the station.

We did not talk to each other. But I was content. I could say my farewells to the familiar sights in silence. But there was something eerie about the train journey. For long stretches Paul and I sat in silence. It was as if this enforced muteness was a kind of dumb show put on by us for the entertainment of others and not for our own safety. It was during this journey that some doubt crept into me about the success of our trip. Not that I could have given any explanation. But when I saw the fat man looking at us, I was certain he knew. The ruin of our undertaking had already been arranged. Looking back, I don't think my suspicion was justified. He probably was not at all interested in us. But he had alerted me. Possibly, we would not succeed.

We had been too optimistic. We never considered failure. We could not imagine what would happen if we were caught at the border. What followed was like a film. I am filming myself and Paul and the parents, as we stroll along the meadows, on a beautiful day in May. The small figure of the guide in front. And then the sudden appearance of the Czech guards, the sandwich lunch in the hut, the car ride, the SS men opening the car doors. But how can one film the lost hope, the complete shift from confidence to despondency?

When we were stopped by the guards, everything was shattered. We had trusted the guide who probably had betrayed us. We think we saw him again when we left the Gestapo Headquarters, a shadowy figure slowly creeping along the edges of the houses, tucking away something into his trouser pockets. Of course, we could have been mistaken. The street lights were not very bright.

It is true that the possibility that something might go wrong had entered my mind in the train. Trying to work out what might happen if things go wrong is the game I sometimes play to help me cope with my worst fears. But I never really believed the Czechs would turn us over to the Nazis. They must have been aware of our panic and tried to quieten us by talking about some paper work which had to be completed in the town. The Czechs had become slaves themselves. We did not know that they had to carry out instructions given to them by the Germans.

My memory of the hours in the Gestapo kitchen will never fade. Without being physically harmed, these were hours of torture. Standing still for hours is not easy. (We must have arrived at that place early in the afternoon and left it when it was getting dark.) But the agony was not, of course, caused by the physical discomfort. The agony was the loss of oneself. Until a short time ago I had been Martin. Now I was an object facing the wall, an object which had nothing to say and nothing to do. Only thinking was permitted. And there was terror in the thinking. What was going to happen to us all? I did not have any illusions. Jews, refugees from Germany trying to cross the Czech-Polish border illegally: concentration camps were instituted for people like us. The Nazis would punish us. What would it be like in such a camp? We knew what was happening inside camps like Dachau. I would survive, I knew, I would survive. But would I wish to survive if mother, father and Paul did not? If only my parents and Paul had not been there. How much easier it would have been to stand and face the wall.

But my mother was the greatest burden in that kitchen. There she stood, for God knows how long before she fell.

My mother, naked.

We were all naked, but I felt dressed.

We were naked because pride and self-esteem had been taken away by that simple command: "Stand there and face the wall." Suddenly we had lost everything. Could I now respect my parents, so humiliated and degraded? It is true, my father had rarely, if ever, exercised his authority over us, not because he was disinterested in his children — he loved us deeply in his own way — but he was too concerned with himself and his failings. But I did look up to him when I was little. He was my father, for me he was the head of the family.

But someone else, a stranger in uniform, had taken over now. I knew none of us could have disobeyed him. My parents had to do as they were told. And I was reduced once more to being a small boy who had been sent into the corner because of some misdemeanour. I did not mind that so much. I did not feel naked. I felt not very different from what I had always felt: the youngest, vulnerable, dependent on my parents and Paul.

My mother, who had always said that she could get on with all kinds of people, my mother, who had always found it easy to relate to whoever crossed her path, my mother, a strong disciplinarian whose wishes had always to be met, my mother had become nothing. Like her husband, she was a failure. How I loved her. How I felt for her. How I wanted to take her into my arms and cry with her. How I wanted to give her back all she had lost. How happy I would have been to show her my poems and the letters from Georg and Toni. How I wanted to cradle her and say: 'I do not mind what you say. I shall accept your anger. I want you from now on to live through me. I belong to you. I want you to lock me up inside you. But get dressed, oh, get dressed, quickly. Don't let me see you like this any longer."

We all knew that it was mother who had fallen. We risked being beaten by turning around involuntarily. At that moment we had perhaps recovered a little dignity. But then we retreated again.

And mother thanked the Nazi for letting her sit down.

"It is very kind of you."

How I hated her at that moment. She played a game. She pacified the bully.

And then Paul, my older brother. He had been made of finer stuff than I. At home on our baby grand stood a photo of him in a silver frame. Paul with his delicate face, flowing blond hair, bare to the waist. And another picture hanging in the lounge: Paul riding a donkey with an expression of slight misgiving. But Paul was not only physically beautiful. His cleverness astounded all the adults. His knowledge, his understanding, his judgement, his scholarship, his musicianship; what an example he was to me. I knew I could never reach his heights. I adored him. I venerated him. His joys were mine, so were his sadnesses. Paul, my big brother, was another father to me, the kind of father my father could not be.

And here he was: my older, beautiful, clever, musical, adorable brother, naked like my parents, diminished and silenced, standing somewhere next to me, but so many miles away. Lost, like the rest of us. Weakened. Feeble. How could I find him again and if I could not, how would I be able to live? Did he know how much he meant to me?

It was not easy to walk into the investigation room with the SS man standing behind me. I don't think I stumbled because I was frightened. Fear had been displaced by the feelings for the other members of the family.

The contrast of the behaviour of the interrogator to that of the SS guard punctuated the unreal quality of that Sunday afternoon. Mental cruelty and grossness and then a kind of courtesy, almost gentleness.

Although confined within a small chalk circle, my heart went out to that benign man behind the desk. I wanted to tell him that I liked him, that I trusted him. 'Do release us,' I wanted to say, 'we are not criminals. We want to get to England. We want to build ourselves a new life.'

He was not the only enemy I loved.

When I returned to the kitchen and did not see my mother sitting in the chair, I thought she had been taken ill and had been moved elsewhere in the house. And then I feared that they had marched her into the courtyard for execution. Perhaps she was going to be the first one and we would follow her one by one. I hardly minded.

Paul stood next to me and I moved my head, almost imperceptibly to catch an expression on his face. He responded with a hint of a reassuring nod. So mother was all right. They must have told her where she was going within earshot of my father and Paul.

It was not long afterwards that they came and marched us out of the building into the street where a van was waiting. It was then that I thought I spotted the solitary figure, our guide, the dark angel, lost and alone, a shadow amongst the shadows of the houses in the light of the evening.

We did not know where we were being sent, but assumed that the destination would be a concentration camp. The sudden comfort of a wooden bench was more important at that moment than what might possibly await us later. Although there was no guard with us, we still did not feel like talking to each other. Perhaps we felt ashamed.

Finally I asked: "Mother?"

I was told that she was being sent to prison. Again we lapsed into silence. It was as if we needed to recover. We had slowly to remould ourselves into our original shapes. We had to become what we had been before.

It was a short journey. A large gate was opened. We got out of the van. Then some keys were turned. We stood in a large hall, full of men, lying on blankets on the floor or walking about. The German guards were in green uniforms — we were soon told that they belonged to the German Protection Police Force which was quite separate from the SA or SS — and seemed to mix informally with some of the internees.

The atmosphere seemed relaxed. Father met somebody whom he had known in the past. From him he learnt that this was no concentration camp in the ordinary sense but a transit camp for those who had attempted to cross the border illegally. We were amazed at the number of people who apparently had tried to escape from occupied Czechoslovakia. There were hundreds here. The camp served a particular purpose. People were being sorted out. Those with a political past — communists and others who had been actively engaged in fighting the Nazi regime or who had been 'black listed' for some reason — would be returned to Germany for punishment. The majority, mostly Jews, so the rumour went round, were being pushed over the border after their 'clearance papers' had arrived here. The camp was a kind of sieve. While waiting for the decision, one had time to pray that nothing in one's past could be construed by the Nazis as an act against the Third Reich.

We were fairly treated by the German police. Physical conditions were most primitive. Food was sent from the Women's Prison (where mother was kept) in large containers and dished out into tin bowls. Some of these had a special label attached to them with the initials 'T.B.' We only hoped they had been sterilised effectively. We gulped down the messy stuff because we were hungry. There was also coffee with a bitter taste. It was said that something had been added to keep us calm.

For the next ten days we slept on the floor. Time was spent cleaning the place, talking to each other and reading. Books were allowed into the camp. Visitors could be seen in the courtyard. Rita, Paul's girlfriend came to see us one afternoon. It almost hurt to see the beautiful girl in such circumstances.

There was no bullying, no roll calls, no interviews or interrogations.

Everybody was waiting.

Everybody was tense.

From time to time somebody packed his things together and left. Sometimes we were told where he was going, back to Germany or across the frontier, more often the man one had chatted with the previous evening had disappeared by the morning.

Somebody, somewhere, made a decision about your life. You were not called to defend yourself. There was nothing you could do to affect the outcome. You had to sit it out. You had to wait.

The men questioned themselves, again and again. People

had become their own judges.

Had you said something or had you done something which could be held against you now? Was there anybody who had envied you? Who had held a grudge against you? You were not a member of the Communist Party, but did you associate with someone who was? Did you leave your affairs in order when you left Germany? Did you take some gold watches abroad to sell them? Who knew about this? What about your neighbours? Were you on friendly terms with them? On too friendly terms? Did you play your part in the Great War? Did you perhaps avoid fighting for the Fatherland? If in Public Service, did you annoy anyone? What was your relationship with your superior? Did you have Aryan friends? Why? When? Did you have sexual intercourse with an Aryan girl?

Was there anyone amongst us who could say with conviction that there was nothing in the past to which the Nazis could take objection? We must all have offended in some way. And yet, many people were let free. What criteria were being used?

There were some who wrung their hands when you spoke to them. Others had a twitch in their faces. Or they stared into space. Or they mumbled to themselves. There were also men who spent much of their time writing down statements defending themselves, although they knew that they would never be read. Men supported each other, although no one admitted to any offence. Everyone had lived immaculate lives.

Paul and I were worried about father. Father had bragged so often to us how he had managed to avoid recruitment to the fighting forces and the part he played in the army medical corps. We knew something about his fruitless efforts to run a business. We were also concerned about the parents' close friendship with the Schillers. We did not think the Schillers would want to testify against us, but 'Uncle' Schiller, now a mayor in a small Silesian town, might be pressed to slander us. And then, we realised that we did not know what had triggered off the parents' sudden decision to leave Germany, just over two years ago. Was it only because father was not

able to make a living any more in Germany? Or had it something to do with Elsie? Elsie, our last housemaid, had made
certain threats. Had this been reported to the authorities?

*   *   *   *

I expect servants often played an important part in the lives
of children. In our circle of friends and relatives, all families
had servants. No household could have admitted to being too
poor to employ them.

We were never well-to-do, although we pretended we were.
Certainly, we had enough money to pay our servants the
appallingly low wages. Next to the kitchen there was a tiny
bug-ridden room for the cook, and when we could still
afford to have a housemaid, she slept in my room with a
screen around her bed. My mother was known to be 'good'
to the women she employed, so we did not have too many
changes.

There was Lotte, the cook, who came to us shortly
after Paul's birth and stayed with us for nine years. I understand there was also a Nanny at that time but she left when it
became clear that Lotte and Paul had become very attached
to each other. It was Lotte who took over Paul's early
education and when at the age of six or seven, Paul started
to show an interest in books, it was Lotte who listened to
him and read to him. I think Paul's knowledge of some of the
German classics stems from those early days. A walk with
Lotte often led to a discussion about a play they had both
read. My mother did not mind. She trusted Lotte completely,
Lotte who was known by everyone as the 'Pearl'. Indeed,
she was the jewel of the family.

Mother told me later that Lotte had loved me too, but
I don't think she took much interest in me. In any case,
I was too small to be able to participate in Lotte's and Paul's
intellectual exercises. I did not make strong demands on her.
I liked to hang on to her as young children will who need to
feel safe. She did not push me away. I am grateful to her for
that.

For many years Lotte was engaged to be married and her
fiancé, Herr Strick, accompanied us on many of our walks.

He was always extremely friendly and behaved in a somewhat formal manner to us children. He respected us as people in our own right and I liked that. But there was something amiss in the relationship between Lotte and Herr Strick. I know mother talked to Paul about it once or twice, but I never understood what it was all about. It looked as if the wedding was never to take place. A date was fixed, then cancelled, a new day for the wedding was arranged, then it was off again. One day we heard that Herr Strick had disappeared. Lotte became ill, probably as a result of the break-up. Her headaches made her scream. She was admitted to hospital and there was talk that her head would have to be opened up. I was very frightened. How could they open up Lotte's head?

The house felt empty without her. For the first time I knew what it meant to have lost something. The housemaid took over Lotte's duties as best she could, but the household had been disturbed. I blamed Lotte for it. Why should she fall ill, and headaches are not an illness anyway. No wonder the doctors wanted to punish her and take out the inside of her head. But how are they going to do it? I felt my skull. 'It is all hard. Perhaps they can do it through the mouth?' And I touched my mouth which had been operated upon several times.

One day mother made me go to hospital with her. The smell of ether. The snaky corridors. The ghostly white-clad people. A complete otherness. It was nothing like the clinic where I had been a patient myself. The small, intimate home-like place where people knew each other and where mother joked with the surgeon. Here was the world of insects, human insects rushing about into strange bedded halls, gleaming floors, blinding lights. It shocked me. I could not talk. There was a woman covered with white as if snow had fallen on her. Her lips widened a little when she saw us. It was Lotte. I could not talk to her. She was a stranger amongst strangers in a strange land. Near her there was another woman who lifted up an arm rhythmically, up, down, up, down. Lotte saw me watching her and she whispered to mother and Paul:

"She is dying, poor dear."

What did it mean, she was dying? One dies when one is

old. I wanted to run away. But I looked at the green smooth lino floor and drew pictures on it: pictures of flowers and trees and mountains and lakes.

Lotte did not need an operation after all. She returned to us for a while but then decided to go and live in London with an aunt. We never heard from her.

I loved Martha who became our cook-cum-maid later. I felt very close to her. She was a small person with a tiny, upturned nose and her eyes always sparkled. She always found time to listen to me. I was not happy at school and could talk to her about it, about how I did not like lessons, how I was bullied because of my ugly lip, how I was longing for the weekends, how I was looking forward to the holidays. Martha never scolded me, she never judged me. She responded in a way that made things easier for me. If I had written any poems in those days, I surely would have shown them to her. We talked about food — a very important subject for me — films she had seen, tit-bits from the local paper, and gossiped about the people who came to visit us. My mother felt, with some justification perhaps, that I spent too much time in the kitchen and that I neglected my work for school. Martha, who was my first adult friend, meant so much to me, that I gladly took the risk of being told off by my mother or Paul.

That she was the cause of the only severe beating I had as a child is not altogether surprising. It was a kind of sacrifice I made.

One day Martha gave in her notice, to my great dismay and to the relief of my mother who was convinced that she had an unhealthy influence on me. Martha was getting married. Soon afterwards she left with a heap of garments from my father's shop: underwear, stockings, handkerchiefs, aprons. My parents were always generous to the servants at Christmas or on special occasions. I was very unhappy for a time. There was no one else to go to now. Paul followed his own interests and had little time for me. At that time I had no friends at school. There was nobody who could take Martha's place.

How thrilled I was when mother read out a letter from her one day, inviting me to come to her flat near the city centre to meet her husband. My mother was not very keen for me to go, but there was no reason to say no. Martha had been a good reliable servant, after all. I was twelve years old and could well manage to make the journey by tram on my own. I was to visit Martha the following Sunday afternoon. How free I felt when I left home. And what a welcome I had. Martha's husband was a plumber. He had rosy cheeks, blue eyes and strong, warm hands. I liked him straight away. And the flat: unlike at home, here everything was well ordered. The new simple furniture: each piece seemed to be standing in its proper place. And there was so much colour about: the bright red bed cover, the flowery delicate curtains dancing in the breeze, the dark blue carpet, the white walls: this was Martha's place. A place which she had created. And everything was so clean and tidy. Why should I have noticed this? I was not a tidy boy. But at home, in the rooms at the back where Paul and I stayed most of the time, and where my grandfather lived, the tables and chairs, the cupboards and wardrobes, the rugs and the beds were an assortment of odd bits and pieces. Nothing seemed to belong together. It was impossible and joyless to keep things tidy. But here in Martha's place all fitted together. There was a feeling of belonging.

The couple were charming. I was treated like an adult. Martha enjoyed being the host and her husband told stories about some of the people he had come across in the houses of the rich.

They took me for a walk along the city moat. Although only a few kilometres from my home, I had never been here. We climbed the tower: the city lay below us. It had lost its threat. I felt like a conqueror. I was in charge of myself.

Martha had made a gateau which she served with whipped cream and real coffee, not like the brew at home, made of malt, which was served to us and grandfather. ("Caffeine is bad for children and the elderly," said mother.) After a game of cards, I said that I had to get back home where I was expected at half past seven. It was nearly seven already. It was not difficult for me to promise to come back again. I had enjoyed myself so much. Maybe mother would allow me

92

to stay one weekend. I could always sleep on the sofa in the sitting-room. I said that I would ask mother.

The couple accompanied me to the tram stop. It began to drizzle and I begged them not to wait and get back home.

Then it rained properly, I had not brought my rain coat with me. Somebody ran towards me and said that there were no trams going South for some reason and that it was best to ride into the centre and go back by a different route.

It took a long time to get home. I was nearly an hour late. At last I rang the bell.

My mother and Aunt Minna, who had never been fond of me, were waiting for me. They gave me no opportunity to explain why I had been delayed. They both screamed and hit me. I felt their arms and hands all over my body. The smacks burnt my cheeks and my ears. I tried to get away from them, but they followed, screaming and hitting me.

"Father has gone to the Police," . . . hit . . . "Paul is looking for you in the street," . . . hit . . . "one hour late," . . . hit . . . "soaking wet," . . . "where have you been?"

Mother's fury was a release from her anxiety, she had lost control. Aunt Minna's fury was her fury towards us, especially towards me who could never love her because I could never be like Willi.

There was no way I could protest my innocence. My mother's anxiety had made her crazy and Aunt Minna still had some scores to settle. Finally they were exhausted. And then it was too late to tell them why I had arrived late home. I did not want to talk about Martha. The injustice hurt more than the blows. When Paul returned wet and pale, I said that I was sorry to have caused him worry. Paul ruffled my hair. He had forgiven me, that was all that really mattered.

Lotte had belonged to Paul, Martha to me and Elsie our last servant had blurted out that she had belonged to father.

Elsie was a tall dark woman who was usually dressed like Aunt Minna, in grey. She had long black hair tied in a bun. She had a slavic face. I think she must have been of Polish origin but she would have denied this. She was approaching middle-age and I did not find her attractive. She was no substitute for Martha and I did not want anything to do with her. Once I saw her in my mother's room in front of the mirror on the dressing-table. She was whispering to herself. 'Like the horrible queen in the story of Snow White,' I thought, 'she looks like a witch.' Another time when I went to her room to ask for something, she was combing her long hair with hair pins between her lips. She stopped when she saw me, took out the pins and said:

"Don't you think I am beautiful, Martin? A black beauty?"

"Yes, you are pretty," I lied. She looked for her purse and said:

"Go and buy yourself some sweets." But I replied that I did not want any and ran off.

After she had stayed with us for a year or so, she packed her suitcase one afternoon. (Hitler had recently come to power.) Then she knocked at mother's bedroom, opened the door and announced:

"I am leaving, Frau Rosen. I am leaving now. My future husband is waiting for me in the street. You'd better give me one month's wages."

"But you have not given me any proper notice, Elsie," mother protested.

"If I were you I would give me the money all the same," said Elsie, "my fiancé is a member of the Party. He is outside, in uniform. You can see him from here, if you care to look out of the window."

"Elsie, this is not the way to behave, surely."

"Let me have my wages and there won't be any trouble."

"What on earth do you mean, Elsie? Trouble? Why?"

"You ask your husband. If I tell my fiancé, who is a big noise in the party how your husband seduced me, there will be trouble, lots of it."

Mother paid, of course. Elsie left at once. Father said that Elsie's accusation was pure invention.

I only heard the full story from Paul in the transit camp when we discussed father and whether he was in danger of being sent back to Germany. Formerly I had thought that Elsie had accused father of shouting at her. I was very naive, but sex had never been discussed in our house. What I knew, I had learnt from the out-of-date encyclopaedia or from boys at school. It would have never occurred to me when I was in my early teens that father could possibly have 'affairs' with women. Other husbands and wives and their affairs were sometimes discussed by my parents, but such a thing could, so I thought, never happen in our family. I knew these were forbidden friendships.

In spite of the quarrels I had witnessed between mother and father, I could not imagine father loving anyone else but mother. It was only later, when I was fifteen or sixteen, that I understood mother's hints. Paul threw light on father's sexual appetites. He was attracted to uncomplicated girls, shop assistants, ticket sellers, factory hands. He was certainly a handsome man and was even good-looking when he was getting on in age.

"People mistook me for Franz de Vecsay, the Hungarian violinist, when I was a young man," father told me once, showing me an early photo of himself. He looked artistic, was smartly dressed and wore a well-waxed moustache.

"And do you think there was some truth in Elsie's allegation?" I asked Paul.

"It is possible, you know. By the way, did I ever tell you, Martin, how shocked I was when as a boy of twelve or thirteen, I saw him once drop a french letter? We were both waiting for a tram. He pulled out his wallet to give me some money for a theatre ticket, and the little envelope fell out of his wallet on to the pavement. I knew what it was, of course. Father was very embarrassed. He knew I knew."

"But what of mother?"

"Oh mother had accepted all this for a very long time. As long as there were no scandals. Anyhow, we are talking about the past."

"But the past is relevant. If Elsie has reported that father seduced her, it does not really matter whether it was true or not."

"Somehow I don't think she has reported it. She was not really a bad woman."

"What do you mean?"

95

"Well, Elsie was a spinster who could not cope on her own. When someone came into her life who actually wanted to marry her, she threw all caution to the wind. If it had been necessary to betray father to achieve her end, she would have done it. But it was not necessary. She just wanted some money."

"I hope you are right. But there may have been other girls father slept with, girls, women, who were not Jewish."

"It is possible."

"So father is in danger."

"Usually women don't openly admit to having had occasional relationships with men."

We saw father talking to somebody.

"Do you think he is worried?" I asked Paul.

"We know so little about father," said Paul, "he lives his own life and does not want us to share in it."

"But sometimes, when he thinks no one is watching him, I can see fear in his face."

"There is fear in all of us," said Paul.

Something happened to Paul at the camp, of no great importance, but it was significant. It concerned me, perhaps, more than him. I was not ready to accept at the time, that Paul in some ways was more fragile, even weaker and less able to cope in particular situations than I was. I had always felt inferior to him, intellectually and emotionally inferior. I bathed in this feeling of inferiority and did not wish it to be different. I wanted to remain the younger brother, the not-good-looking little boy, the pupil with limited attainments, the adolescent who had not yet become a man. I wanted to continue to be Paul's disciple. His opinions were also mine, I never doubted his judgements. For me he was always right. When I saw him facing the wall in the Gestapo kitchen I felt more humiliated than he did, I am sure.

There was another occasion – it almost seems now that it had been arranged for my benefit – when I was forced to witness how vulnerable Paul could be, how small and feeble in the eyes of others, in my eyes.

A large space of the walled-in camp – a former factory

building – was reserved for walking about, as we were not allowed outside for exercise. The floor had to be swept every day, and the guards saw to it that we took turns in the cleaning operation. Six of us were given brooms and a can of water for sprinkling. It was not an onerous task, and did not take us very long.

There are some simple physical actions which some of us cannot perform. I, for instance, have never been able to fling a pebble into the distance as I have seen boys do on so many occasions. They throw the little stone across the lake and make it kiss the water several times before it sinks. I have practised in secret, but to no avail. I am just not able to cluster all my energy into my fingers so that it is possible to propel the pebble with all the necessary speed.

Paul could not manage the regular round broad sweep with the broom. He was noticed by one of the guards.

The guard called a companion. The men came from all corners of the hall to watch. Paul was given a lesson. A lesson in sweeping. The two policemen gave instructions. There was no malice. They did not bully Paul. None of us, witnessing what was going on, made fun of Paul. It was certainly not funny. There he was, standing on his own on the concrete floor, holding the broom. He was told what to do and how to do it, directed by the guards, encouraged by the bystanders. But he failed. Again and again he failed. He held the broom too stiffly in his hands as if it were a strange tool to be used for an unknown purpose.

I could not bear it any more and walked away. How ashamed I felt for Paul. How could he be so stupid. Anybody knew how to sweep the floor. Sweeping is a natural movement. Why was he not able to do it? Surely, he was clever enough to work things out. If you move like this and then like that, the broom will do its work.

"Again," I heard the guard shout, "do it again. Bring your left hand down."

I could not see my father. I blamed him and mother for never having given Paul the opportunity to practise.

'Why must the Nazis be his teachers?' I thought.

The German guards were stern but patient.

"Not this way. I told you before, you must lift your elbow

e

a little. That's better. Do it again."

Paul, my big brother, was shown up as a moron, my Paul, an idiot. But then my anger turned into compassion. I thought I knew how he must feel. I knew how I would feel in his place. Shamed and degraded. Once more naked. And I wanted to run out to him, take away the broom from him and shout at the guards:

"You leave him alone, will you? You know nothing about him. He is much cleverer than you. And he is valuable to me, you understand? If you are destroying him, you are also destroying me."

I prayed silently: "Please, let it be over quickly."

When finally the guards had lost interest and the people around Paul had dispersed, it was as if nothing had occurred. I was prepared to face Paul who would come over to me presently, his eyes full of despair. But Paul did not seem at all disturbed. He joked about the incident as if it had happened to someone else. When I tried to express my concern, he could not really comprehend it.

I soon became aware that my distress was not his.

I had transferred my own feelings on to Paul.

A few days later my father was informed that he and his wife had been 'cleared'. They would be allowed to cross the border. His sons would follow them in a day or two. This splitting up of the family we thought to be typical Nazi chicanery. Perhaps this was so, but Paul and I had reason to be thankful later. If we had stayed together, it would have been much more difficult to endure the ordeal.

This was the plan: We had to get to Kattowitz, report immediately to the Refugee Organisation there and obtain through it a 'certificate of stay' authorised by the British Consulate. Such a certificate would ensure that we would not be sent back. (The certificate, we were told, would confirm that we were waiting for a permit to enter Great Britain. The Polish authorities were being asked to agree to us remaining in Poland until the entry visa arrived and suitable transport could be laid on.)

It sounded simple enough. The parents, who would arrive

first in Kattowitz would make frequent enquiries about us. The Zimmermanns and the Loebs had already promised to look after the whole family. We had nothing to worry about.

Father was in high spirits. Now that there was no danger of being sent to a concentration camp, his old optimism had come back.

"I shall look after mother," he said, "don't worry. And we shall see you both very soon."

Paul and I were on our own. It was a little painful not to see father in the evening, next to us, huddled up in blankets. Two days later we left the camp. At the Headquarters of the Police Department, we were photographed and our finger prints were taken. We also had to sign some papers, saying that we had no intention returning to Germany or to any country occupied by Germany. Our passports were returned to us. Exit visas had been granted. There was also the remark that re-entry was forbidden. We were instructed that we had to report to the nearest borderpost, should we be caught by the Poles and sent back by them. We hardly listened. We expected to be with the parents that evening.

It took us a week to reach Kattowitz.

There was a musty smell in the long room. A smell of leather boots, sweat, and carbolic soap. Soldiers marched in and out, saluted, spoke loudly and laughed. The brothers were being ignored. They sat on wooden seats holding mugs of coffee.

The Poles had not been unkind.

As on previous nights, the brothers had heard a sudden shout in the darkness of the night. They froze, praying there would not be a second shout. But there always was another shout.

"Halt."

Then, as before, a quick walk under escort. Usually to army barracks. Interviews with the Polish officers were businesslike. They knew what it was all about. There was the fear of a German invasion. The Polish army was manning the frontier. The Germans sent undesirable people across the border. The Poles did not want them, they sent them back. The brothers were told that this was not the time for Poles to look after refugees. The German threat was real. There could be spies amongst these Jewish refugees. One could not take any chances. The Poles did not want them. The Germans did not want them. It was a kind of game. The Germans threw the Jews one way, the Poles the other.

The officer who spoke to Martin and Paul did not put it quite like this. He seemed to be well educated and did not wish to give the impression that he was an anti-semite. He spoke good German:

"You must understand. We can't care for thousands of people who are chucked out by the Germans. They are not our responsibility. You must go back and tell them that we have no room, no room at all."

"But we do not want to stay in Poland," said Paul, "we want to get to England."

"Have you got permits to enter England?"

"Not yet. But we shall get them when we are in Kattowitz."

"You are hoping to get them, you mean. But hope, my friends, hope is not enough. Stay here for half-an-hour and then we shall take you to another spot. It will be easy to get back to Czechoslovakia from there."

Paul explained that they did not wish to go back. They would have to report to the Czech or German frontier guards and the whole thing would start all over again.

"This is Czech business, not ours. Poland is not a dumping ground for people who are not wanted. I am sorry for you both, but I have my orders."

Martin said: "It does not really help to be sorry. Can you suggest what we could do?" There was a slight irony in his voice.

"It is not for me to make suggestions. Perhaps you can hide somewhere with a Czech family. Keep away from the Germans. They will soon forget about you."

The officer did not understand. It was impossible to explain the situation to him.

"Can't you just let us go?" said Martin, "our parents are probably already in Kattowitz and waiting for us."

"That is very unlikely," the officer replied, "we are

catching all of you. Nobody can succeed in crossing the border unnoticed. The Polish army is in readiness."

Soon afterwards the brothers were driven by car to another place a few kilometres away. They were told to walk in the woods. They would soon be back in Czechoslovakia. It was useless to argue. This had already been their third attempt.

Paul said: "Of course, they don't understand. One can't really blame the Poles. It is all so pointless. We shall have to report again, wait until nightfall and try again. Only to be stopped and sent back."

"We shall make it eventually."

"Can you see us doing what we are doing now for another week or two, or three, or a month?"

"Well, we aren't very clever at it, are we? There must be a better way. We shall learn from our mistakes. My friend Toni would know what to do. Going back, it does not matter where and how we walk. It's getting to the Polish side undetected which is the difficult bit."

"I don't think I can carry on for much longer, Martin."

"What do you mean? The parents are waiting for us. They are expecting us."

"We might not be able to make it."

"Of course we shall make it, Paul." But Martin was not convinced.

The night was clear and cool. In the distance there was a small light.

"This must be the Czech post," said Martin.

"We'd better go and report," said Paul.

They knocked at the door. It was opened by a German in SS uniform.

"And who are you?" asked the storm-trooper with a hateful smirk.

"Paul and Martin Rosen reporting," said Paul. "We were sent back by the Poles, Sir. We have been ordered to report to the nearest frontier post."

"Come in, come in," the man replied sarcastically, "the kettle is boiling. Coffee is nearly ready. We have been waiting for you." He called out: "Two friends come to visit us." He turned to the brothers: "It's a bit late for a party," and looking at his watch, "nearly three o'clock in the morning.

Never mind, we shall have a good time, all the same."

'Have I not heard all this before?' thought Martin, 'of course, it was the witch who invited Hansel and Gretel into her Gingerbread house.'

The hut was sparsely furnished. A table or two, a few chairs, a poster of Hitler.

There were three uniformed young men. They opened their arms in mock welcome. They cried out:

"So happy to see you both. It is good of you to come and see us."

The brothers were very frightened.

One of the men suddenly cleared a table, pushed it into the middle of the hut and shouted:

"Get on this table, you two. Be quick about it."

The brothers obeyed. 'Now they are going to hit us,' thought Martin.

"Name?"

"Paul Rosen."

"What?"

"Paul Rosen." (Laughter.)

"And you?"

"Martin Rosen.

"Wrong. Both wrong." (Laughter.)

"You are Jewish swines, right?"

"We are Jewish, yes."

"Jewish swines. How should you report?"

"Jew Paul Rosen."

"Better . . . and you?"

"Jew Martin Rosen."

"Father's name?"

"Leonard Rosen . . . I mean Jew Leonard Rosen."

"Mother?"

"Jewess Sarah Rosen."

"Where are they?"

"They crossed the border. They are probably in Katto-witz."

"That's where you should be. You stupid asses. Can't manage without Mum and Dad." Turning to Paul: "Say: I am a Jewish dope."

"I am a Jewish dope."

102

Turning to Martin: "Say: I am a Jewish idiot."

"I am a Jewish idiot."

"What is your father?"

"My father is in business."

"A businessman? He cheats. All Jewish businessmen cheat."

"He does not cheat, Sir."

"Of course, he cheats. Say: My father is a Jewish swindler."

"My father is a Jewish swindler."

"He has swindled the German people. Say: My father is a Jewish scoundrel."

"My father is a Jewish scoundrel."

"The Germans are getting rid of swine like you and your father. What is your mother doing?"

"My mother is with my father. She is not doing anything."

"Wrong. She is a sow. What do sows do?"

"I don't know, Sir."

"Sows rake about in the mud. Your mother is a sow and gave birth to you both. Say: My mother is a sow."

"My mother is a sow." (A biff from behind.)

"Louder. Louder. So that we can all hear."

"My mother is a sow."

"A Jewish sow." (Turning to Paul.) "Shout out: My mother is a Jewish sow."

"My mother is a Jewish sow."

"And you? What is your job."

"I was a student, Sir."

"A student? A student? And may I ask Herr Student what he has been studying?"

"I was a medical student in Prague, Sir."

"You Jewish scum, a medical student?"

"I had to give up my studies.

"Give up your studies? Killed some people, didn't you? Knived them?"

"No, Sir."

"Cut up some Aryan girls, didn't you?"

"No, Sir. I could not continue studying. I did not have any money."

"I see. Good job, too. Jewish doctors are murderers. Did you murder anybody?"

"I was not treating patients yet."

"Thank heavens for that." Turning to Martin. "And you? What did you do?"

"I helped my father, Sir."

"Helped your father? What kind of help?"

"I wrote letters on the typewriter for him."

"Writing letters. Cheating people. All Jews do." Turning to Paul. "When did you sleep with a woman last?"

"Two months ago, Sir."

"You are a fucker. Say: I am a Jewish fucker."

"I am a Jewish fucker."

"Was it with an Aryan girl?"

"No, Sir."

"You are lying. All Jews are liars. We have means of finding out."

"She was a Jewish girl."

"A Jewish girl. What was her name?"

"Rita. Rita Lewin."

"Rita Lewin. Did you rape her?"

"No, Sir. She was my girlfriend."

Turning to Martin. "When did you play with yourself last?"

"A week ago, Sir."

"A week ago." (Laughter.) "For the likes of you, every day, with a glass of water." (Laughter.)

Then, abruptly, the brothers were ordered to get off the table. They were taken to the door and directed to walk together outside. For a moment Paul thought they were going to be shot. Martin saw that the sky showed signs of morning, a mild wind blew in a new day. Paul and Martin did not look at each other. They were embarrassed. Then Martin spoke quickly.

"They are going to question us separately and will ask each of us what we were talking about."

The brothers agreed that they would say that they had been treated fairly, that it looked as if it was going to be a nice day, and that they were hoping to get to Kattowitz at the next attempt, that they were looking forward to

104

meeting the parents again. The whole family was looking forward to starting a new life in England.

Martin had been correct. The brothers were interrogated separately. The guards seemed to be satisfied wth their replies which were identical: fair treatment, nice day, must get to Kattowitz, meeting parents, on the way to England.

The sun was rising. There was some traffic of peasants and cattle. The brothers were ordered to sing.

The brothers sang in harmony:

"When all the little brooks are flowing,
then I must go a-wandering,
when my love is far away,
I shall seek another."

"Nobody can say we are not treating you Jews properly," said one man.

And then:

"I knew a comrade,
a better one you will not find
a drum was beating for the fight . . ."

"Not this one," a man called out, "are you mad? This song is for Germans only. Sing another one."

"God favours him
whom he send into the wide world.
He will show him his marvels:
The mountain, the valley,
the stream and the meadow."

The brothers felt almost happy. Another odd thing: some-one brought coffee and rolls, still warm.

"We got them from the village. Freshly baked. We look after our Jews, you know."

'What is this all about?' the brothers wondered.

A little later the officer who had been the most objection-able only a short time ago, took them aside and addressed them.

"So, you are on your way to England, angel-land. Hurry up and get there. Poland is no refuge for you. The German soldiers are only waiting for their boots to come back from the cobbler and then we shall be over there." He pointed through the window. "Get to England as quickly as you can."

105

"We hope to get the permits as soon as we join the parents," said Paul.

"And send me a card. I mean it. I am serious. A view of the Thames and the Houses of Parliament. You understand? I want to know that you arrived in London. I like London. I spent a week there a few years ago."

"To whom shall we address it?" asked Martin. He did not sound impudent. The officer wrote down his name and rank and the address of the border station.

Then it was time to leave. They were going to be sent to another crossing point along the frontier.

Paul and Martin stood to attention.

They said 'good-bye' and 'thank you'.

It almost sounded as if they meant it.

The attempt to reach the Polish side during the next night was again unsuccessful. In the early hours of the following morning they reported to Commander Schulz who was in charge of the frontier post. Commander Schulz remembered the parents who had passed through here some days ago.

*   *   *   *

Mother later admitted that Commander Schulz was the sort of person she had always been attracted to. Tall, muscular, civilised, meticulously dressed in his black uniform, showing strong white teeth when he smiled, smelling of Eau de Cologne, always obliging, especially to women, he could be said to be the typical Prussian Officer.

"I have always had a weakness for such men," said mother to Paul, "and father will bear me out when I say that we have to thank Commander Schulz for being able to cross the border without any trouble at our first attempt. Believe me, Paul, he was charming to us. He took us in his car for miles to a hidden spot. We could not fail to get across to Poland from there. We clearly saw the lights in a cottage, as he said we would. He assured us that the people living there would make all the necessary arrangements. So it was. Commander Schulz is no Nazi, of course, he belongs to the old school, a German through and through, a true Prussian, "honourable and trustworthy."

"It sounds as if you are talking about Uncle Schiller," said Paul.

"Well, Uncle Schiller wasn't a Nazi either, as you know."

"But Uncle Schiller did not behave honourably, neither was he trustworthy."

"Circumstances can change a man, Paul. The Schillers were in a terrible domestic situation. For them it was a matter of surviving or going under. Uncle Schiller felt responsible for his family."

"So you are excusing the Schillers for what they did to you and father."

"I am not excusing them but I can understand them now. I understand why he had to join the Party."

"And you think Commander Schulz became a Commander in the SS because there was no other way for him to provide for his family?"

"Well, of course, I don't know that. I had a serious discussion with him. He said that he believed Hitler would not last, but that he was useful at present in waking up the German people and making them aware of their strength."

"But you do know, mother, what he really meant? A need for power and dominance."

"I don't think so, Paul. I think he meant something finer, something more civilised."

"But mother . . ."

"Believe me, Paul. Commander Schulz was a highly intelligent man. He spoke of the need to develop a national conscience."

"What on earth does that mean? It's clap-trap, mother. And you fell for it. Did you by any chance ask him what he thought about the treatment of the Jews in Germany?"

"I could speak quite frankly to him. Father was surprised that I dared!"

"You dared, indeed. Father should have stopped you somehow. It was naive of you, to say the least, to involve yourself in discussion of this kind. He could have all of a sudden shown a different kind of face."

"But you see, he did not. He knew to whom he was talking."

"To whom he was talking?"

"I am a Jewess, I would not deny it, but I am not the sort of woman the Nazis would ill-treat."

"Mother, you are living in a fool's paradise. You should have witnessed how they treated your sons at one point."

"I don't want to know, Paul, don't tell me. But I am sure Commander Schulz had nothing to do with it."

"No, he didn't. But he could have."

"Commander Schulz told me that he has had Jewish friends."

"Yes, like the Schillers."

"He said that in his opinion the Jews have got a part to play in the reconstruction of Germany, not at the present time, of course, when the situation is so fluid, but later. Jewish culture has got a contribution to make, he said, as long as the Jews are not trying to take over German culture. He felt that the Jews had penetrated too deeply into all fields of German life, and I am inclined to agree with him. Now there is a strong resentment and reaction from the Germans."

"Surely, mother, you can't believe in all this nonsense."

"Paul, there have been too many Jews in high positions in Germany. I know what the situation was like in Breslau. The majority of doctors and lawyers were Jewish. My fellow-believers are not the most modest of people. They tend to push themselves forward. And their behaviour often leaves much to be desired, you must agree. Jews are often loud and noisy. And you know how they talk about the gentiles, 'the goyim', as if anyone not a Jew is somehow inferior. We Jews have ourselves to blame for much that is being done to us."

"You talk as if you were an anti-Semite yourself."

"Well, I could not help agreeing with Commander Schulz that we Jews are not without blame. He said I was the first Jew he had met who saw matters so clearly and that if everyone, every Jew I mean, were like me, Sarah Rosen, there would be no need to take action against them."

"Schulz told us he had met you and that you had probably managed to get here without difficulty. My impression of him was rather different from yours. I thought he was a slimy character. He hid his real self behind a mask of amiability. He wanted to discuss the poet Heine with me and why he thought Heine's art was degenerate, but I was not having any of it. I said 'yes' to everything he said. As I had no intention of entering into an argument with him, he soon gave up. He passed us over to one of his underlings who at least left us alone. Both Martin and I needed sleep badly. He did not take us in his car in the evening but accompanied us with his Alsation to the crossing point. Then he called out: 'Run.' We ran straight into a group of Polish soldiers. We were sent back the next morning. Isn't it strange, mother, that you were attracted to him, and you are quite right, there is a similarity between him and Uncle Schiller."

"It was you, Paul, who compared him with Uncle Schiller."

"But it was you who was also attracted to Uncle Schiller."

*   *   *   *

My parents joined the 'Odd Fellows Lodge' merely for social reasons, I am certain of it. My father was a kind and even generous person, but I do not think he believed in an institutionalised 'brotherhood'. I remember he made fun of the initiation rites to which he had to submit himself as a new member. ("It is all very secret. I must not tell you what was happening. They played a record of the 'Magic Flute' — Mozart, isn't it? 'In these Holy Halls — in this temple there must be no vengeance!' Believe me there was as much ill feeling amongst the brothers there as anywhere else.")

But the parents made new friends in this modern building. It was a kind of social club where the amenities were excellent for special events and informal get-togethers.

This is where the parents met Herr and Frau Schiller.

The couple were of a similar age to my parents. Otherwise they did not seem to have very much in common with them, at first sight.

Herr Schiller, a Protestant, had been a pilot in the Great War — a member of the famous Richthofen Squadron — and Frau Schiller had been a teacher in a girls' school before her marriage. Herr Schiller was the co-director of a furniture firm. Frau Schiller looked after two daughters, the older one was my age. Gertrud's sister Senta was much younger.

My parents and the Schillers went out together, to restaurants and night clubs — all four enjoyed eating and drinking — and soon they became very close. Herr Schiller was my mother's 'type' and my father enjoyed the company of the attractive tall blonde, Frau Schiller.

My uncles and aunts were shocked. Such a friendship was unheard of. The Schillers could not possibly be accepted to 'our circle of friends'. Not only were they not Jews, but they were so typically German, he a former officer of the air force, she a German woman with aristocratic looks. Why were the Rosens so attracted to them? Anti-Semitism was already ripe in the late twenties. Was it not best to keep to one's own kind? Nothing good could possibly come out of such a close liaison. The oldest brother of my father had a word with the parents, but he was probably told to mind his own business. Not only marriages but friendships too, seem to be made in heaven.

My mother was always delightful when she had a little too much to drink, she started to philosophise and Herr Schiller — my newly-found 'uncle' — hung on her lips as he listened to her views of life in general, on Beethoven in particular, on the state of the world. He was enchanted by her free and easy manner, her wit and the unorthodox views which she often expressed. She in turn had someone else to talk to — Paul was, after all, only thirteen. She had given up a long time ago trying to have a serious conversation with her husband. Herr Schiller was a German of the best kind, a gentleman with excellent manners. My mother was happy. I wonder what my father saw in Frau Schiller. No doubt she appealed to him. It was her gentleness, perhaps, her lack of aggression, so unlike his wife, which drew him towards her. She did not rebuke or reproach him for past failures. I imagine they told each other the stories of their lives and probably enjoyed themselves, discussing with each other their spouses.

The two couples spent more and more time together. No day passed without some kind of rendezvous.

I did not see much of either Gertrud or Senta. They went to school in a different part of the city and we only met when I went with the parents to their flat or they came to us. Paul, of course, was too old to have anything to do with us young ones. I can't say I was particularly fond of Gertrud. After all, she was a girl, and my experience with Paula who lived in the flat next to ours, had already taught me that it was best not to get too involved with girls.

On the occasions when Gertrud and I did play together, we usually squabbled and Gertrud would run to the grown-ups and complain about me. But I do remember one winter's day when the snow had transformed our tiny bare garden — if one can call it a garden — which encircled the house, into something beautiful. Gertrud and I were building a snowman. We must have been so involved in rolling and patting the malleable snow, that Gertrud had not taken heed of the call of nature. Around her the white turned into bright yellow. She wept bitterly. I touched her flaxen pigtails.

"Never mind," I comforted her, "it will soon snow again and everything will look as before."

She cried and ran indoors, where, I have no doubt, her father showed himself to be the other kind of German, less likeable, less civilised.

Herr Schiller treated his wife and his daughters as his subjects. Perhaps he imagined he was still in the air force. He was in charge. The other members of his family were of lower rank. He commanded and expected that his orders would be carried out without question. His wife dealt with him by usually conceding to his demands without protest. But his insistence on immediate obedience often frightened his children. I did feel sorry for them at times, at least my parents were generally not unreasonable. When Uncle Schiller spoke sharply to Gertrud or Senta, they started to sob and were then sent out of the room. Of course, children were expected to behave well. But Herr Schiller's authoritarian manner, his insistence on immediate compliance to his demands, his shouted-out orders as if he were in the barracks: these were much in contrast to his charming manner which

111

my mother found so appealing. Uncle Schiller was a bully. I know that my parents had words with him about the way he was treating his daughters. I doubt whether he took much notice of their pleadings.

I did not like Uncle Schiller. He probably did not care much either for Paul or me. He would have preferred to have two sons himself instead of two daughters. But we were no substitute. We were too soft for him. He could not shape us into tough youngsters who would stand to attention when spoken to.

Paul was not afraid of him.

Paul already held definite views on subjects like capital punishment, patriotism and war. These, Uncle Schiller must have found very distasteful, to say the least. When Paul argued, mother was sitting next to him, smiling and feeling very proud. But Uncle Schiller was not the kind of person to give up easily. If our parents were unable to give us the education fitted for German boys, then he, Uncle Schiller, would have to do something about it.

I remember one Christmas. We never had a Christmas tree at home and only decorated the table and the presents for the servants with branches of fir on which angel's hair was glittering. The Schillers celebrated Christmas properly. On Christmas eve we went to them and after the traditional dinner — karp with sweet raisin sauce — the door to the lounge was opened. There it was, the beautiful tree, with real candles lit and decorated with gold and silver trinkets. After we had all sung a few carols, it was time for the presents, These were arranged in small heaps on the floor around the tree. Paul got a large book. A book illustrated with many photographs. He opened it and stared in astonishment. There were dozens of pictures of executions: men and women hanging on trees or standing in front of brick walls blindfolded with soldiers aiming their guns at them. Paul had been given a book on how spies had been dealt with during the war. My present was a model castle with a working draw-

112

bridge and many horses pulling different sorts of guns and cannons. And lots of soldiers, of course.

I never played war. The castle became a stage, the soldiers were turned into actors. My games had nothing to do with fighting. Uncle Schiller wanted to toughen us up, he fought a losing battle.

My mother assured us later that there was another side to Herr Schiller. He was a man torn in two, she said. Part of him belonged to the German national tradition, but he was also a rebel who could not conform easily if such conforming could impair his personal moral code.

I am certain mother was right. Uncle Schiller was split in two. But when Hitler came to power a few years later, he did not have the courage to stand up against the Nazis.

His furniture firm became bankrupt. He had saved little and the Schiller's financial situation soon became desperate. There was no income. The parents probably helped a little but our own situation was precarious. Now the Nazis were here, father's business was likely to fold up. Perhaps we would have to emigrate.

I don't know how the link was made between Uncle Schiller and the Party's District Leader. Uncle Schiller was certainly not in sympathy with the Nazi doctrine. Perhaps it was a former war comrade who had brought the two together. Uncle Schiller was offered the post of mayor in a small Silesian town. (A mayor in Germany was an appointment to the Civil Service.) There was only one condition. Uncle Schiller had to join the Party and his daughters had to become members of the Hitler Youth. The Schillers did not make the decision lightly. There were many painful conversations with my parents. But the parents were, of course, not in any position to give advice. The Schillers did not wish to give up the friendship with the Rosens. But both families knew that acceptance of the post must also mean a complete break in the relationship between the two families.

When Uncle Schiller became a Party member, he was forbidden to have any contact with us. I think he still met my father occasionally in secret and his wife came to see my mother sometimes in our house. Uncle Schiller was not strong enough to decline the offered post. This was the opportunity for him to settle down as a respected minor official. He was ready to swim with the stream.

"But I always knew there were signs of weakness in him," said my mother later.

"I wonder what you would have thought of me, if I had done what he did," said my father, looking at mother, "you always say the first duty of the husband is to provide for his family."

Paul butted in: "Surely there are limits to what one can do in all conscience and what one can not do."

Neither Paul nor I had felt any affection for the Schillers, but we were both aware of the tragedy of the situation. There had been real love between these four people. They were deeply hurt. Their way of life had collapsed.

My mother became very ill. One evening she was unable to lift herself from the armchair. The slightest movement caused unbearable pain. Any assistance we offered was rejected with a scream. Mother refused to get out of the chair for two or three days. Her legs swelled up. On advice by the doctor we had to use force and pull the poor woman towards the bed.

I shall always hear her screams in my mind.

She had been turned into a suffering beast.

When I returned from school the following day, a Sister from a Catholic order was sitting near mother's bed. Clasping a rosary, her lips moved silently. My mother too, was silent. I went to my room and did a little work for school.

Then mother's yells shook me.

I stopped up my ears with my fingers.

I cried, but my cries were full of anger.

I wanted to rush to her and order her to stop.

Did she not know what she was doing to me? There could be no pain so strong that one could not control one's shrieks. Was mother out to punish me? Was it so important to be clever at school? Was it not enough to have Paul, so good looking and brainy, always ready to talk with her? There is no one else here but Sister and I. She had no need to prove to me how sick she was. It was the fault of the Schillers, not mine. Why does she want to make me feel bad? Her yelling is for my benefit.

Doctors came. She was examined during the short spans when she was free of an attack. They talked about an inflammation of the sciatic nerve. But they were not sure. They shook their heads in disbelief and went. She was given pills and injections, but the attacks came regardless of the medication. Sister took the place of father in the double bed. Father slept on the sofa in the lounge. He spoke little, mother's illness had affected him much.

One day when she was quiet I went to see her.

She said: "Sit by me, Martin. Believe me, things are better when you are around. Push another pillow behind my head. I did not know anything about pain until now. If you could only believe me, all of you. How can I convince you? Giving birth is nothing, I assure you. I don't think I shall ever be able to walk again."

"Where is Sister?" I asked.

"I sent her out for a little walk. The poor dear can't be imprisoned here day and night."

"What does the Sister do? I mean, why is she here?"

"She is a good nurse, Martin. You can't expect father to look after me for twenty-four hours, day in, day out. But you know, she gives me peace. How can I explain it? When she kneels before she comes to bed and prays, something seems to pass from her to me. It's difficult to describe. Her prayers help, you know. I don't really believe in a God. If there was a God, why should I have to suffer as I do? I am guiltless, everybody knows that. But she believes in Jesus. I get a little faith from her. It comforts me. Can you understand this?"

"Yes, I think, I can."

"I thought you would. By the way, Aunt Schiller was here this morning. You see the flowers over there? She brought me those."

"But, surely, the Schillers don't live in Breslau any more?"

"There was some kind of Party meeting here yesterday. She said she saw Hitler."

"She saw Hitler? What about him?"

"She told me what they say about him is true. To see him is to believe in him."

"Sister believes in Jesus and Aunt Schiller in Hitler."

"She said to look into his eyes means that one commits oneself."

"So Aunt Schiller has become a Nazi."

"I don't know about that. I don't think the Schillers will ever become proper Nazis. But Hitler has put a spell on her, no doubt about that. Gertrud and Senta don't like being in the Hitler Youth. But they have no option."

"And Uncle Schiller? What about him?"

"We did not talk about him. I did not really want to know. You'd better go back to your room now, Martin. I feel the pain is coming, please go . . . go.

Mother was screaming.

One day everything was over. It was as if the pain had burnt itself out. Mother learnt to walk. After a few weeks she was well again.

There was no more news about the Schillers. My parents learnt to live without them. Most evenings they stayed at home.

*   *   *   *

"What do you think about the sudden change in the attitude of the guards towards us?" I asked Paul.

"Well, it was odd. But your idea to prearrange what we were going to tell them about what we had said during those few minutes outside the hut was brilliant."

"Surely, Paul, they were intelligent enough to know that we were having them on?"

"Perhaps. But they probably did not feel very secure. They made us sing because of the people outside. To show how well we were being treated."

"And the breakfast? Why should they have bothered?"

"Well, it is difficult to understand human beings."

"Could it be that they felt sorry for us after the terrible

116

time they had given us?"

"I don't know, Martin. I really don't know."

"What about this strange request that we should write a card from London? They could not possibly imagine that we would do such a thing. It is ludicrous."

"People are ludicrous."

"Perhaps they were worried we would tell about our interrogation when we reach England."

"Perhaps they had just become human."

"All of a sudden?"

"There is a look in your eyes, Martin, a certain glint sometimes, which disturbs people."

"You're joking, Paul."

"No, I'm not. Perhaps you are able to tell them something which words cannot do."

"It's not like you to be fanciful, Paul."

"Do you think we shall get to Kattowitz eventually?"

"Of course, Paul. I am sure."

But I was not sure.

I don't remember very much of our various attempts to cross the border. It is not that this particular episode is unimportant. On the contrary. It was the prelude to what was to come. Later I saw it as a preliminary training. Training in the experience of anguish, not training in becoming more competent in dealing with situations which require initiative. But I could not have imagined that this sort of experience could ever be repeated in some form.

I was eighteen. My life had not been an easy one so far. I had always been conscious of the disfigurement in my face, there were tensions within the family, my education had been interrupted and I had become a refugee when I was sixteen. The belief in myself, my faith, so far untested, in a personal divinity, my romantic attitude to nature: all this was suddenly being questioned. Anyhow, that's how I felt. I was meant to face the world now, not the world which I had created in my isolation as a child, not the world of the 'boy poet', not the world where there were happenings outside oneself which one could accept or discard, but a world of which one was part. I could reject it. But such rejection could mean death. Although there were occasions later when the idea of ending my life did enter my mind, such a resolve was never likely. Slowly I was building up strength within me, strength which, my friend Georg had warned me, I needed to find to sustain me. I learnt slowly.

In the Gestapo HQ I had seen for the first time my parents and Paul as people, people who were as vulnerable as anyone else in spite of the authority they represented to me. My mother said 'thank you' to the SS guard for letting her sit down. She ingratiated herself. But did Paul and I not do the same when we agreed that we would both say how fairly we were being treated, in spite of the mental torture we had undergone, because we hoped they might stop tormenting us? Paul's inability to use the broom the right way. Why should this have caused me such agony? He did not feel degraded when he was instructed in using it. I did. Why should Paul not fail in something, why should he be even an efficient sweeper? Why did I need such make-believe?

Kindness and unkindness. Cruelty and compassion. This one is kind, that one is cruel. This one cares about you, the other does not. Oh, how easy it is to classify people. I almost wanted to embrace the man at the Gestapo place, because there was some gentleness in the way he talked. But he could also be harsh, surely, even cruel? And these fellows at the border station: Why did they make us shout out those horrible things about the parents? Why? Why? Could they also be loving to their girlfriends, to their mothers?

And looking at ourselves: Why were we so truthful? Why did Paul talk about having slept with Rita? Why did I tell them when I had masturbated last? We could have made things up. We did not. The guards had become our judges, it was pointless to lie to them, they could see into us, they were angels, dark angels to whom we had to give account of our actions. People use us, but we also use people. We create them. We make them ugly or beautiful, attractive or hateful. But people are all these things. I have to learn to accept them with their perfection and blemishes. I have to learn to accept myself.

118

To be a Jew. What had been done to the Jews in Germany during the past five years did not make me feel different from what I had felt before. The 'Sturmer', (an anti-Semitic paper read by the boys in school,) the anti-Jewish demonstrations, the racial laws, the concentration camps: in spite of what I knew was happening, I still felt outside it. It did not happen to me. There were Georg and Toni living in Germany, they did not seem to suffer. There was nothing to their letters which gave me anxiety. Grandfather was being looked after by the family where he now stayed. He was being left alone by the Nazis. He wrote that he was content. Things were going to change. It was only a matter of time and Hitler and his gang would be annihilated. Everybody said so. I was German. Jewish, of course. But a German. I had said so at the Maccabi Club in Brünn. I had not changed my mind. Until now. Until very recently.

Who are you?

I am the Jew Martin Rosen.

And your father?

My father is a Jewish swindler.

And your mother?

My mother is a Jewish sow.

Louder. Louder.

My mother is a Jewish sow.

Standing in the kitchen, facing the wall, and then on the table with Paul, silent in one place, shouting out in the other, I learnt my lesson.

I am a Jew. Not because the others said so, full of disgust, but because I am now taking my share of the suffering. My association with Germany can not be refuted. But I am carrying the Jewishness within me. Martin Rosen has accepted it: he is a Jew.

We did not keep a diary of the many attempts to cross the Czech-Polish frontier. I do not think I discussed it much with Paul later. It was a painful experience because Paul and I were on our own and neither of us knew how to act in such a situation. If only someone had guided us, told us what to do and how to do it. I assured Paul that we would succeed

119

in the end, but I was full of doubts. We tried again and again, but we were always caught. The hateful word: "Halt!" still rings in my ears. Held, returned, put into a cell, a hut, a room, escorted to another spot in the raven black hostile landscape, crouching down, hiding, creeping in thickets, stumbling, stopping, listening, standing still, standing still, still. "Halt!" Dejected, we followed those who had rifles slung over their shoulders. We pleaded with them. We begged. In vain. All in vain. Back the way we came or by a different route. We reported: "Yes, Sir, the Germans sent us over." Or: "Yes, Sir, the Poles sent us back." Or: "No, Sir, we are not smuggling anything. We are refugees. Jewish refugees from Germany."

Another try. Another useless try. Night. Stars. Where is East? Where are we? How can we find out? There is a building. We must slink around it. Stillness. Then a bark. Oh, these barking dogs. They might jump at you. Stop. Beams of light. Torches. Down. Throw yourself down. No, run. Down. A searchlight. A sound. A cat, only a cat. Cats bring bad luck when they run across your path. Hush. Hush. Somebody is talking. Now it is quiet. Drops of rain. Rain. Trees. We must not get too wet. It is getting lighter. We must make ourselves invisible. Please, don't let us be seen. "You there, come out." Run. Let's run. "Stop, you two." "We are reporting back, Sir. Paul and Martin Rosen. We are Jews." "I am Commander Schulz. Your parents managed it."

Another attempt. "We won't give up, Paul. The parents are waiting for us. What about walking along this road?"

"But this must be one of the main roads across the border. We should avoid it."

"It does not really matter. Let's go along here, Paul."

"You remember that elderly German guard?"

"He reminded me of grandfather."

"He said: 'How can one treat people like this. Like cattle.' "

"He said that?"

"Not all Germans are Nazis."

"There is the barrier in front of us. Let's avoid it. Across this field here, along the hedges. Then we can hit the road again somewhere."

"Where does Czechoslovakia end and Poland begin?"

"We must be in no-man's-land."

"Why don't we stay here?"

"What do you mean?"

"We'll just lie down here."

"We shall starve."

"Someone will come. The Red Cross, perhaps."

"No, no. Let's carry on . . . the barrier is behind."

"Are we in Poland? There is an old man. Shall we try to walk round him?"

"Ask him. practise your Czech. Ask him whether we are in Poland."

"Excuse me, is this Poland?"

The man nodded.

Poland. We had made it. There was a house a few hundred yards away. We could see its red roof. We had stopped talking. How was it possible we had succeeded? Walking along the main road, just steering clear of the frontier barrier. Just ambling along like Sunday trippers because we were too weary to play the cat and mouse game again. From then on, matters were taken out of our hands. All that was necessary was done for us. A telephone call. We were given something to eat. A car. The drive to Kattowitz.

We saw father outside the Refugee Centre.

"There you are," he called out, "we were wondering where you had got to."

Mother said later: "There is nothing worse than separation."

I felt very close to the parents.

How was it possible that I once contemplated emigrating to Palestine?

Fear in darkness. Waiting for the rain to stop. Dogs barking. Trembling bushes. Terror in being. Friendless beams of light. No songs. No poems. Where is He hiding? Where is my God hiding? Is He still in me? Why did He leave me stumbling and blundering in the wilderness? I was alone without Him, alone with Paul who was alone. Will I still be able to love what I had loved so much before? The blue or

121

f

grey or black skies? The skimming birds, the sailing butter-
flies? The plants, the blooms, the richness around me? The
hills and the views into the valley?

What had happened to the world which I had created as a
child? Had I been robbed of it now? What was to take its
place? Something bitter, no doubt, something bitter. Something unfeelable, untouchable, uneatable, unlivable.

One flash back: a time we had spent in a police cell. If
you stood on tiptoe you could see a small patch of the
market square. People wearing coloured clothes coming from
all directions, streaming towards a particular point. I could
not see it. What was it? Bells. Church bells. It must be
Sunday. I could not tell Paul, not even Paul, but I was happy.
There was joy, somehow. I remembered something I had read
in school. Not that I remembered the lines, I was never good
at learning verses. But I remembered the feeling. The feeling
of an Easter day, a festive day, a Sunday. Goethe's Faust
spoke:

". . . bells already tell with vibrant drone / the solemn opening
of the Easter Mass . . . / Why seek ye, heavenly sounds so mild /
and mighty, me in dust distressed? / Go sing tender souls are dom-
iciled. / I hear but lack the faith, am dispossessed / And faith has
wonder for its dearest child . . . "

Continue to sing for me, sing for me.

In spite of the growing political tension, the weeks in
Kattowitz were enjoyable. Unlike Paul I did not follow the
news closely. I was not frightened by rumours and in any
case we would be in England soon and war between England
and Germany was unthinkable. I was happy to take over
from my cousin Willi, who once again had entered my
life, the secretarial work for the local Refugee Committee.

We were fortunate, of course, being cared for by the
Zimmermanns and the Loebs. We did not have to join the
groups queuing for meal-tickets, clothing vouchers, accommodation.

I felt important writing out the lists of those who would
next travel to London. Willi had already left. One day the
names of the parents were on the list.

122

Mother said that she was not going to London without us. She seemed determined. My father was distressed. Why were Paul and I not on the list? Through a Committee member the British Consul was contacted. His reply was that he had no jurisdiction in such matters. Decision rested with the Home Office in Whitehall. Father rang his nephew Bruno, the barrister in London, and was advised by him to come to London, now he had obtained the permit, and ask for a personal interview with the Home Office official.

Mother was finally persuaded to accompany father.

"We shall see you very soon," father said, "I shall not leave any stone unturned."

Mother wept.

It was strange to spend the next weeks without them.

We did not get our permits.

War broke out.

III

CROSSROADS

Two skies. Above: gold and a red shimmer. Light blue patches. Behind: a black and brown blanket. It was not only the quintet which was leaving the town. There was a snaky line of men and women and children walking across the meadow, carrying bags or small cases. One thought was in all their minds: to get away, to get away before the Germans arrived. Soon the stream of fugitives thinned out. Everybody had been advised that it was better to split up into small groups than keep together as a mass of people. German pilots would be able to spot an unending caravan. It was best to lose oneself. The quintet, of course, kept together. Rudi and Ernst took the lead, Franz, on his own, walked a little behind them. Then there was a gap. Paul and Martin made up the rear. They had little to say to each other Ernst had suggested walking to Radom, about seventy kilometres from here. Ernst had a map. One only had to follow him.

"I wonder what we would have done if we had not met the others," said Paul.

Martin shrugged his shoulders. But he was very grateful. He did not think they would have been able to manage on their own. Memories of the border crossing flooded him.

The long march had begun.

Later in the morning the quintet rested. A tallish, bearded young man came up to them. The conversation with him was mostly in mime. By using his whole body he made it clear that he had escaped from a prison and was on his way to the

124

capital. He offered to lead them.

'Another guide,' Martin thought and he could not help smiling to himself. They walked for a while and came to a barbed wire fence which blocked the path. There was a warning notice. They assumed that this was a military zone and that it was not allowed to pass through it. But the self-appointed leader found an opening and beckoned the others to follow him. The path continued on the other side of the fence. There was nobody to be seen. Then a small village. It was completely deserted. All of a sudden the guide grinned, waved and disappeared into the bushes. There was nothing else to do but to walk on. They passed the empty cottages, the boarded up shop, the soundless school.

A single soldier came towards them.

He ordered the group to follow him.

At the nearby military post he made his report.

Paul, who was the only one in the quintet who could understand some Polish because of his knowledge of Czech — Franz, who had lived in the German-speaking part of Czechoslovakia, spoke no Czech — tried to explain the situation. Martin thought:

'All this has happened before.'

Then Martin's face was burning. He had been slapped. He looked into a face full of anger and hate.

"You filthy German," the soldier shouted. Paul did not translate this. The soldier swung out his arm again but another soldier prevented him from striking.

The quintet had to join a small column of soldiers. They marched to Szydliovec. It was evening when they were handed over to an officer. He looked extremely smart, not at all like a fighting man. He sat behind a table and manicured his fingernails. He questioned the boys in fluent German. He listened to their explanations patiently. He said that he sympathised with them. They had to get away from here. The Germans were expected here soon. Perhaps tomorrow. "Get to Radom as quickly as you can," he said, "perhaps you can get transport there. But don't lose any time. Go."

He put a cigarette in a long slender holder and lit it. "Best of luck."

"Thank you. Thank you, Sir."

125

A few more kilometres. Another village. Night. An empty school building. Exhausted, they were looking for the entrance. They had no strength left. None of them could have gone on. They found a classroom. They stretched out under the benches.

'I would have never imagined,' thought Martin, 'that a school could become my refuge.'

The next day they reached Radom early in the afternoon. They saw the town from a little wood through which they had come. They heard screeching sirens in the distance, and then the dark song of the planes, the whistling of the dropping bombs, the explosions. They settled down under the trees, there was no point walking into Radom now. They waited. When it became dusk they entered the town. It was late already but everything was in uproar. The population was being evacuated. The town was burning.

The boys queued to obtain vouchers for a train to Deblin and then waited for it all night. Early next morning it arrived.

But the train halted after half an hour. There was some confusion. It was said that the train would return to Radom. Some passengers got out and quickly dispersed. The boys decided to get off as well. There was no point going back.

They spent the day in a little forest not far from the railway line. There was a feeling of light-heartedness in the group. The weather was fine. The trees gave shelter from the burning sun. Martin was reminded of holidays spent in the Silesian mountains when he was a child. Paul talked to Rudi about school days.

According to Ernst, who studied the map, they were on the way to Warsaw. The German army obviously had not broken through as they had feared. This was the seventh day of the war. The Poles must have good defences. This was not just to be a 'walk-over' for the Germans as in Czechoslovakia. One had all reason to be optimistic. It was important to stay together. In Warsaw it would be possible to get to England by plane.

In a clearing there were two villas with gardens surrounded by firs. Franz offered to go and ask for some milk.

126

There was no one at home in one of the villas.

A lady answered the door of the other.

"Foreigners?" she called out. "We have nothing here for foreigners. Go away at once or I shall call the police."

All the cheerfulness evaporated. The quintet had become very quiet. Feeling low, the boys lay under the trees and fell asleep.

It was Franz who heard the chuffing of the train. They ran to the unmanned little station. Indeed, a goods train had stopped and the boys climbed up a cattle truck. But there was already somebody inside. The man shouted and was brandishing a revolver. The boys jumped back on to the platform. The train departed without them.

There was only one thing to do: to walk along the track to Deblin. At least there was no danger of one losing one's way. It was a clear night, the moon and stars gave off some light.

When they reached the outskirts of Deblin early next morning, there was again the familiar racket of droning planes and screaming bombs. A peasant gave them something to drink and bread.

"We must not stop here for long," said Rudi.

"It is still a long way to Warsaw," said Ernst looking at his map.

"I don't think we can possibly get to Warsaw," said Paul.

"You thought differently yesterday," said Martin.

"I am inclined to agree with Paul," said Rudi, "we won't always be able to explain to people who we are and what we want."

"Perhaps we should try to join the army," said Franz. It was not often that he spoke.

"It is a possibility," said Ernst, "perhaps there is a Czech Legion."

"Does this mean we are giving up the idea of getting to Warsaw?" asked Martin.

"I don't think we have much choice in the matter," replied Rudi, "for the Poles we are Germans, their enemies. How can we convince them that we are on their side, unless we join the army and fight with them? Franz is right, we should try to enlist. At least we shall be safe then."

"Safe from what? Safe from the Germans?" Paul asked,

127

irony in his voice.

"Safe from the Poles, at least," replied Rudi, "just now they are more menacing than the Germans."

The others had to agree. It seemed the best action to take in the circumstances. Of course, there was the danger of being captured by the Germans. But it was best not to think about that. At least in the army one would be fed and clothed and what was even more important: one would be told what to do.

Franz went with Rudi into the town which was still smouldering, to make some enquiries. The others waited.

Franz returned, alone.

"Give me your papers," he said, "Rudi is with a major who will see to it that we get enrolled. There are other people as well. We have to get to the military authorities in Lublin."

The boys gave Franz their passports and also the notes from the British Consul which confirmed that the holders were awaiting visas to England.

Rudi could give little additional information when he came back with Franz. It was all a little odd. Some foreign military group was in the process of being formed. But one had to walk to Lublin. The major who was holding the papers was to lead the group of volunteers. They would leave in an hour's time.

"How many kilometres to Lublin?" asked Martin.

"About sixty," replied Ernst.

"This means we can't reach it before tomorrow night if we walk smartly," said Franz, "unless we are lucky and get a lift."

"At least we have an aim," said Martin.

"We shan't be staying for long in Lublin," said Paul, "I expect we shall be sent to the front straight away."

"At least it won't be up to us," said Martin.

*   *   *   *

I was, of course, aware of the seriousness of our situation when we started on our long trek through Poland on the 5th September, leaving behind us the shattered town of

128

Kielce. And yet I was not depressed. On the contrary. Strange as it may seem, I felt something like elation. Perhaps I could prove to myself that I was now able to cope with anything. And then, Paul and I were not the only ones. There was the group. 'Fate is not something outside me,' I thought, 'I must not say, here I am, do what you will. I must make an effort.' It was wrong to hand over responsibility to a force outside oneself. This time, I hoped I would work towards success. I would not hand over responsibility to God. It was an angry God. He did not wish to have anything to do with us. The sun signals another day in summer, a day like any other day in summer. The sky will soon swallow up the black smoke from the burning houses behind us. There is the field: the corn already cut and stacked. Here a bush with yellow blossoms. A speckled bird. A patterned butterfly. God does not concern himself with us. He leaves us to ourselves. We shall get to London and be united with the parents because of the actions we shall take. We are our own Gods. Decisions will be shaped by us. I felt free. I had grown up. I was a man. The fancies of boyhood I had left behind. Life was good, yes, good.

Would I have thought like this if I had been alone with Paul? And did I not feel in the very depth of my being that not everything depended solely on me? Had I altogether shaken off my faith in a divine guidance? I was still a child, in need of a parent, but I rebelled.

I read through Paul's diary again. Of course, I remember the events very well. Have I not relived them so many times throughout the years? The drama is still vivid. But I am saddened that hundreds of details have become blurred. What is left are the outlines. What did the people who played such an important part during this time look like? So many have become shadows.

Rudi I remember. I remember his fragile body, his delicately featured face. But then I had known Rudi when I was a child. Mist covers Ernst and Franz. Ernst was stocky and Jewish looking, Franz tall and fair with an open friendly expression. I cannot visualise anything else. When it comes to the others who crossed our path — the escaped prisoner or the Polish officer who behaved like a dandy and the many men and women who like bright and dark angels talked to us, looked at us, touched us: I can only remember their actions, how they behaved towards us, little else. And even some of the things which people did to us I can only vaguely recollect. If Paul had not written in his diary 'Martin was beaten' and reminded me of the enraged soldier, I would probably have forgotten all about this incident. Somehow it was not important enough to remember. Or the long slog along the railway track to Deblin. I can recreate the atmosphere of this particular night but I cannot recall the five of us trudging between the rails, presumably listening for the rumbling or the whistling of a train. I wish my memory would serve me better. Because, looking back, I recognise that there was nothing, not anything at all, which was without significance. How much more I could learn and perhaps understand if I could project these five weeks — weeks of great weight — onto a screen like a film. But no, I could not bear it. These thoughts are fanciful. Everything is well arranged. I remember as much as I can carry.

For instance, I remember the empty schoolroom where we had spent the night on the way to Radom. Next morning I noticed the sums written up in chalk on the blackboard and saw the small red ball in the corner of the room and a sentimental holy picture, and the wooden thermometer hanging beside it. Once again I smelt the familiar smell of old wood, unwashed clothes and the biting disinfectant used for cleaning.

*   *   *   *

Paul was already in the top form of his Junior School, when I started my own education. I was five years old.

The year I spent in the kindergarten I enjoyed. Although I was clumsy, I liked cutting out pictures, pasting and sticking them on thin blue cardboard. Raffia work was too difficult for me but there was something satisfying about weaving strips of coloured paper into a prepared paper loom. What I delighted in most were the rare occasions when we were allowed to use the furniture — benches and tables and whatever else was available — in building up houses or

130

cars or aeroplanes. Over these strange concoctions we threw blankets and old curtains and even our own coats and scarves. Then I could sit somewhere near the ceiling and feel powerful. The two ladies who ran this private establishment to get us used to school life were most kind but perhaps not very wise. Music and dancing, dressing up and building houses did not form part of a school curriculum in Germany.

Paul was clever, the family knew, relatives and friends knew. No great hopes were set upon me. Martin was no Paul. And yet, I wanted to show them all that I was just as clever as Paul. I also wanted to be praised. There I was: holding my mother's hand, the satchel smelling of new leather on my back with sponge and slate hanging from it and clasping a large decorated 'Zuckertüte' (the coloured conical bag full of chocolates and sweets, the traditional present given to a child in Germany on his first day at school).

I intended to work hard and be like Paul.

And indeed, the first end-of-term school report was very promising. My mother cried for joy. The comments were glowing: 'Excellent in everything Martin attempted. I hope he will carry on like this.'

But the remarks in the following reports became less favourable: 'Not as good as previously. Flagging, why?'

By the time I had completed my elementary education, the standard of my work was no more than satisfactory.

I was not Paul.

The rector of the school, Herr Gerber, who was also my teacher and more interested in the intricacies of German grammar than in the children he taught, was not particularly fond of me. I can hardly blame him. Not only did I show little aptitude in the construction of sentences, but I could not have been a pleasant child to teach. This was not due to lack of intelligence, I think. I just did not like lessons and although I wanted to be popular with the boys (there were no girls in our class) and adults, I could not get on with people. But perhaps most important was the fact that I needed time for myself. To have to spend so many hours at school was an imposition. I needed time to idle. I also felt I was an outsider. I was usually aware of the physical blemish in my face and when I was not, the other children reminded me. Often I was made fun of and mother came to the school and complained and that made matters worse. I had never been taught to stand up for myself. No, my mother did not help. Because of her anxiousness for my health, my physical health, I was not allowed to take a full part in what was going on outside school hours. Only when the weather was fine, could I go on school trips. I was not encouraged to join in sports. In winter I was too warmly dressed. My mother, no doubt well intentioned, insisted that I should not be exposed to possible illnesses or accidents. Unfortunately, in this way, she singled me out from my peers to a greater degree perhaps, than the unsightly scars on my face.

To the great surprise of everybody, I passed the entrance examination to the Grammar School 'with flying colours'. At least this is what Dr Rindel told me more than once when I was obliged to walk with him to the stop of the tram. Dr Rindel dwarfed me. This incredibly tall man was on the teaching staff of the Grammar School. He had also been one of my examiners. He and his very delicate-looking little wife lived in a flat in the house opposite to ours. Throughout my years at the Grammar School he made me feel guilty.

"I hear you got another bad mark in German. How is it possible? You did so well at the entrance examination."

Or: "What was your summer report like? Poor? And we had such great hopes."

Or: "I am sure you are not working enough. I saw you playing in the street yesterday. What a shame, considering your good potential."

Or: "Your brother is doing so well. Why can't you copy him a little? I know it's in you. What is needed is more effort, my boy, more effort."

I tried to avoid Dr Rindel in the mornings and walked smartly. But he, with his long strides, usually caught up with me.

"I say, my boy, how are you doing nowadays?"

I was not doing well at all. I was a very poor pupil at the Grammar School. If Paul had not sometimes supervised my homework (I hated to sit down to work at home), my parents would have probably been asked to take me away

132

from the school. With Paul's help I just managed to scrape through. Until disaster struck. I had to repeat the third year. I was not going to be moved up into the lower fourth. It did not really come as a surprise. My parents had expected it. There were no reproaches. They had been surprised at the time that I had been admitted to Paul's school. Decision had been made many years ago that I would work with father in the shop. I was never regarded as bright enough to go to university. As long as I could write a decent letter (good handwriting was important) and knew how to do additions and subtractions, all was well. Father, certainly, did not demand more of me. One clever son was sufficient. Mother too was not particularly interested in my school progress. Neither parent put any pressure on me.

But to have to repeat the year was a great blow to me. I felt humiliated. I sat at my favourite place on the window-sill at home, looking at the letter from the Herr School Director which had been sent by post, and wept, wept all afternoon. Mother and Paul tried to comfort me, but to no avail. I cried my eyes out. It was not that I would miss the other boys from the class — I had not made any close friends — or that I dreaded doing last year's work once more. I did not much care what the uncles and aunts would have to say. But I felt that I was a failure.

Everything to do with school: teachers and children, the building, the classrooms, the playground, learning, memorising, tests, homework, the stink in the lavatories, walking to the tram stops on early dark mornings, the daily imprisonment, the sarcastic remarks by the grown-ups, the bullies — it is true, I was a victim of bullies — the ink stains on my hands, the sweaty smell of the changing rooms, the hateful lesson in physical education, sitting in desks which were too low for me, the handing in of work, the handing out of corrected work, the calling out of names — "Rosen, decline 'hortus', the garden, for me," — but also eating dried up sandwiches in the playground, sounds of shouting, the ringing of bells, screeching chalk, books slammed on desks. I hated it all with a hatred I cannot put into words.

Still, it hurt me to know that I was a failure. I had been singled out. And I wanted so much to be like the others.

But my last year at Grammar School proved to be the most important one.

Although Georg and I had been in the same schools and in the same classes throughout, it was only now that I became close to him in spite of him having moved to a higher form. I cannot remember how this came about. It is odd that our friendship deepened now, when we were physically separated during lessons. Toni, a year younger than I, had lessons with me. I was attracted to him because he was everything I was not: good-looking, keen on sports, independent, a member of the Jewish youth movement, popular with everyone. I longed to be like him. One day I dared to speak to him.

"I should like to join the Jewish youth movement."

He replied that he would talk to the group leader, a young man of Paul's age who was a pupil in the same school.

I can still see Toni in the playground talking to him, pointing to me. The group leader looked in my direction. He shook his head very slightly. I was not accepted. Toni ran to me and said that he was very sorry.

"Can we meet one day after school?" I asked, hoping against hope.

"Sure," he replied, "let's go swimming together, tomorrow."

At least I was good enough to become a friend.

In my last year I spent most of the 'breaks' on the second floor in the modern annex of the school which seemed quite empty. (Only the art lessons took place on the first floor.) Here I could look out of the window onto the street and watch the people passing by. There was stillness around me. The din in the playground did not penetrate into the corner of the window where I was hiding. Apart from an occasional hooting of a passing car, the window-pane shut off the noise from the world outside. It was as if I watched a silent film. Looking into the sky, the ever changing heavens, beyond the glass, beyond the street, beyond the tops of houses, how I yearned for the time when I could be free and live the life of a poet. I had just started to write verses. These I had shown to Georg.

"You are gifted," Georg had said, "you should get down

134

on your knees and thank God."

And I did.

We had to salute our teachers at the beginning and at the end of each lesson in the Nazi manner. (Jewish teachers and pupils were exempted from bellowing out: Heil Hitler.) Boys came to school in their Hitler Youth uniform. I was little affected by this. It did not concern me. When at the end of the school year the 'numerus clausus' was put into force — only a limited number of Jewish children were allowed to remain in State Schools — I was glad to leave. I attended for a year, classes specially arranged for those who like me had been 'chucked out'.

My father thought it would be good preparation for a business career, if I took a course at a Commercial School. To our surprise I was admitted. I was the only Jew in the school. The other boys in my class did not take much notice of me. I shone. I was the best pupil in the class. I was happy. Happy in school, for the first time. A new teacher arrived. He stood in front of the boys and made a little speech.

"I am not just your teacher. I want to be your friend. I am not here just to show you how to do your book keeping. I am also your adviser. Your counsellor. Trust me. Come with your problems, whatever they are, I shall always listen to you and help you."

I went to the teacher after the lesson.

"I never heard a teacher talking like that," I said to him, "I shall come to you if I need some help."

The teacher asked: "You are a Jew, Rosen, aren't you?"

"Yes, I am," I replied.

"What I said does not apply to you, Rosen. I cannot consider you to be my friend."

I was shattered.

A few weeks later another teacher gave us some work to do at home. It was an essay on advertising. My imaginative writing had never been appreciated by the teachers at the Grammar School. Here was my opportunity. I could create something. I wrote a composition in dramatic form. It was read out in class. I was expecting praise but I was

135

told that I could not possibly have written this and that I had copied it from somewhere. I was told to own up. I said that this was my own work and that nobody and nothing had helped me. The teacher did not believe me. The other boys laughed. I was told to stay behind after school and write another composition under supervision. I ran home and told my parents. They decided I should not go back.

My formal education was completed.

* * * *

The empty classroom.

Putting my jacket on the floor under one of the benches to make a pillow for my head, I thought:

'It is better to lie under the bench than sit on it, in spite of everything.'

The Polish episode was dramatic. I was one of the principal actors. An adventure film which does not ring quite true. Was it really I who walked for miles and miles in a war ridden country, a country attacked by those who were also my enemies? One could bear hunger or even thirst, but what was almost unbearable at times was the knowledge that we did not belong anywhere. The Poles, too, regarded us as their enemies. Our situation was the drama, not the extraordinary incidents which a film director might wish to exploit. How can one present the inner drama to an audience? How can one express in words and pictures what one feels: lost, rootless, cast out, forlorn? But there were moments of hope too. They were triggered off by a remark, a memory, a scent in the air.

The little forest where the sun caressed the trunks of the trees: it reminded me of the holidays I had spent when I was little.

* * * *

I lived for the school bell to ring at lunch time. Lessons finished at one or two o'clock, as is customary in Germany. To be released, to be free. But I still had to avoid the bullies in the street waiting for me, then the tram journey home, and a warmed-up lunch, some inescapable homework — done hurriedly unless Paul sat next to me — and then: liberation. The rest of the afternoon was mine. To play in the street where I was — unlike at school — at least suffered by the more robust children. I was happy to be told what to do. Or to go on my scooter and later for longer trips on my treasured bike. On rainy days to play with blocks and sticks and plasticine and, when I was older, to go and see Georg or Toni or in hot weather to visit the open air swimming bath. I loved to swim. It was the only sport I was reasonably proficient in.

Then the day came when I could say: "Tomorrow is the beginning of the holidays." My longing for freedom from school was so intense that it made me feel ill at times. I am sure it was unlike the usual pleasure of anticipation enjoyed by other children.

I threw the satchel into the darkest corner of the wardrobe where it could not be seen, changed my clothes, then sat on the wide window-sill in my room, looked into the clouds and exclaimed: "Thank you, thank you very much." It was going to be my tomorrow, my days after tomorrow. All next week would be mine — and sometimes more than one week, and in summer several weeks.

My parents did not insist that I should do some work for school during the holidays. They had long ago resigned themselves to the fact that their Martin was a gentle simpleton. They let me be. I cannot remember that I ever opened a textbook during school vacations.

I could be myself and that meant that I did not do very much. I liked to sit and look or play quiet games which had no meaning for anyone else. I could not be persuaded to pick up even a simple children's book. Paul nearly despaired. He certainly tried many times to convince me that reading gives pleasure. Perhaps it was because I associated reading with school work that I refused. For some reason father intervened once. Probably mother had impressed upon him that he should use his authority. Father ordered me to read one of Karl May's adventure stories — a fat volume, over six hundred pages long. I had to give him an account of the

137

story when I had read it. I cried and pleaded, but to no avail. 'This time,' I thought, 'the holidays are spoilt.' But I had to admit, I enjoyed the long narration and read others by the same author, who always wrote about his personal extravagant exploits. (Like others I lost faith in Karl May later, when I learnt that he had always been a sick man who had never left his study.)

We often spent the long summer holidays away from home. The packing and final arrangements frequently led to arguments between the parents, grandfather and Paul. I witnessed these with trepidation, wondering whether we would actually get away. I was relieved when I saw the porter employed in my father's shop taking the enormous trunks to the station.

The station: smelly, dirty, steamy but filled with so much promise. And then the snorting of the train when it finally left. (Will it ever leave? Will grandfather, who had to buy cigars at the kiosk, get on it in time? Why is mother angry?) So slowly at first, after a little while quicker and quicker until I could make out the definite rhythmic pattern to which I found words.

When I was a little boy we stayed for several summers in Agnetendorf, a small place which was nestled amongst the Silesian Giant Mountains. Lotte, our beloved cook, came with us. We looked after ourselves. Now we had our own house like the Lindens. It was situated next to a fast-flowing stream. Here we would stay for several weeks. Bliss indeed. The mountains seemed to be so close that I thought I could touch them, if only my arms had been long enough. And over there amongst the trees lived a great man, I was told, his name was Gerhard Hauptmann. He wrote plays which were being performed in the theatre. Under no circumstances must he be disturbed. He was sitting at a large desk and wrote. There were dogs in his garden which bit people who entered. No talking was permitted when we approached his house on our walks. If he heard us shout, he might come out and wave his stick at us. Or, perhaps, he might let the dogs loose. There was a wall around his garden. I wanted to climb it to see what was on the other side. But I did not dare.

Oh, there were trees, so many trees, thousands of them, not just a few as in the South Park at home, but countless trees with needles instead of soft leaves, as if they wanted to protect each other from the light. They stood so near to each other. And their scent. There was nothing like the scent of fir trees, sweet and god-like, mysterious. Just to be amongst them, in the forest, and to breathe it in with eyes shut and then open them and watch how the sun was slipping in secretly and painting the trunks with dark shadows. And then the soft carpet of millions of shed needles and the unfamiliar forest sounds of birds and other creatures. Perhaps there were bears? Somebody had said there were still bears in the Silesian Mountains. I was afraid of bears.

But there were the grown-ups here who would see that I did not come to any harm. Only father had gone back home to look after the shop. He would come again for week-ends and would inquire whether I had been good. (There was always the hidden threat that he would take me back with him if I misbehaved.)

Walking. Climbing. Perhaps to a waterfall, or to a mountain top. Or to a castle ruin. The Kynast or the Kynsburg. A lady in white had disappeared, many years ago, had disappeared into a deep well. She had been in love with a knight, but the knight loved another lady. I looked into the deep abyss, hoping to see her, shivering, frightened. Was there not a sound coming from the bowels of the earth?

Always well marked directions painted on boards or little arrows stuck on trees: 'To the Spindlerhütte – 2½ hours.' It took longer, it always took much longer.

My mother was keen on digging out one of those small tender fir trees, fenced in with scores of others in a nursery of tomorrow's Christmas trees. She wanted to have one of them, take it home and plant it in a pot.

"Please don't," Paul pleaded and I aped him:

"Please don't."

We had to stand guard.

I was not only afraid for mother. I was also afraid for the young tree which mother dug out with her bare hands.

"The tree will look nice in our wintergarden," mother said,

"you'll see." She climbed back over the low fence onto the path and hid the ransacked spiky plant in a large bag which she brought with her for this purpose. I was certain policemen had been hiding amongst the trees and were going to rush towards her at any moment and take her away to prison.

The end of the excursion. The beauty spot. A view into the valley. Or the foaming tumbling mass of water. Or the disappointing clammy mist on the ridge of the mountain. And always mountain huts or cafes with milk for me and a fizzy apple drink for Paul.

Then the quick descent. The toes pressed against the shoes. This hurt. "Don't run. Walk."

We ran. Sometimes we leapt across streamlets. On and on. We rarely fell. Until we got to a main path. We waited for the grown-ups.

We sang. Wanderlieder. Folk songs. Mother had a good voice. She was happy when she sang. It was good to know she was happy, she was not often happy.

Return to the house, our house. The smell of wood and goats. Lotte had made a thick soup. Then milk pudding.

The sky darkened. Lights shone through the dusk from the mountains. Like stars. People lived there, high above, amongst the clouds. Tonight the air was transparent.

Next day it rained. The mountains were blotted out. Sheets of fog. Greyness all around. Paul was not in a good mood. He sat by the window and read. He did not want to be bothered. I wanted to be an ice cream man. Soap, lots of lather. Newspaper cut into squares. I ran to Lotte: "Have some strawberry ice." To mother: "Chocolate for you." To grandfather: "Vanilla for you." To Paul: "You like coffee ice?"

"Don't be a nuisance, Martin. Can't you see I'm reading?"

My ice cream melted almost as soon as I had portioned it out. Damp bits of paper all over the place. Grumbles. This is not our house, we can't do as we please.

Not our house? Of course it is ours, for a long time yet, for weeks and weeks. It is our house.

Will the rain never stop?

But one year the coach-driver who had fetched us from the

station, told us that there had been a disaster a few months ago. A violent storm had destroyed many houses.

"You know the hotel by the river?" he said. "Well there was a wedding celebration going on. The storm ripped it in two. Some people lost their lives. The falling bricks killed them. Others were swept away by the waters. The water was a beast, I have never seen anything like it, you know. And I have lived here practically all my life. And the rocks and boulders which came hurtling down from the mountains. It was a terrible night, believe me. This place will never be the same again, I'm telling you."

I understood. The weeks here would not be the same again. Nothing can ever be repeated.

There was the feeling of death. There were many scars left from the havoc. This tree broken down, that house sliced into two halves where a woman had been rescued from under the debris.

'People were probably dancing in the hotel, dancing and singing and having a good time, and then all of a sudden there were cries and screaming and wailing,' I thought.

I heard their shouts: Maria, where are you? I am bleeding. The boulder, the boulder lies on my feet. Come, help. Will somebody lift me? Are you there, son? Are you alive? Speak to me, for heaven's sake, speak to me.

I wanted to weep because of the loss. The loss of my paradise. The little stream next to the house was filled with great rocks which the storm had brought down from surrounding hills. Much of the time was spent by Paul and two other boys easing rocks away. They wanted to clear the stream of obstructions. These were lonely weeks for me. We did not often go for walks and many of the familiar paths were still blocked. Paul rarely played with me. But on one occasion when the other boys were away, Paul turned to me and said: "Let's play horse and driver. I am the driver."

He wrapped around my hips the cord of his mauve dressing gown. He, the coachman, held the ends. We trotted along to Hauptmann's house, a man watched us. We had stopped running. I lifted my legs as high as I could, as I had seen horses do at the circus, and brought them down very slowly and silently. The great man behind the wall could not possibly

141

hear us, or was this the great man, standing there and looking at us? But he could not be, he looked like an ordinary man.

I nearly drowned in the stream when it was cleared of rocks and stones, now very deep in places. I thought this was death when the water was swirling and gurgling around me. All was green and bubbly. One of the boys pulled me out. My mother rushed out of the house, gesticulating. I was put into bed. Concerned faces. I was wanted and loved. It was good to be alive.

Some years we spent our holidays in spa resorts. Not to 'take the waters', of course. I cannot understand now why the parents chose one of these places which had so little to offer us. There they were, all these people, the sick, the not-so-sick and those who imagined they were sick, the middle-aged and the very old, promenading, grasping their glasses of sulphurous liquid, or listening to music in front of the pavilion, (classical music played by the Silesian Philharmonic,) or taking the air in the spa park, or in the Rose Garden, or strolling along the avenues or lying in deck chairs, wrapped up in colourful blankets. No child dared so much as cough between noon and three o'clock, the 'quiet hours' when no noise whatsoever was allowed.

And yet even here I found riches. Not only because of the walks when there was so much to see, to smell and to touch, but the day's programme, so different from the routine at home, made it all worthwhile. There were these men and women who could be watched without them taking notice of me. The opera singer, for instance, who made an effort to be recognised. Or the baron with his monocle and his bright yellow walking stick who looked so superior. Or the lady who sat at the same table as we did in the small hotel; who was given raw liver (just slightly browned on the top) every lunch time. "I need iron for my blood," she said.

My heart went out to her.

I had just recovered from a skin infection. I had been away from school for a few weeks, but mother wanted to take me

142

with her to Bad Pyrmont, a spa in the Weserland, where the parents of Uncle Schiller were running a boarding house. The school medical officer could only be persuaded with difficulty to agree to my convalescence. He did not think this was really necessary, more time from school was not warranted. But my mother smiled at him and when we were ready to leave, he kissed her hand and said:

"I know you will take good care of him, Madam. He needs plenty of fresh air and wholesome food."

My mother had won the day, as usual.

It was autumn in 1929, I was nine years old and I would have to pass the entrance examination for the Grammar School next year. I was behind in my school work, but the parents were not too concerned. A few extra weeks away from school would not make much difference. They did not think I would be able to pass the examination anyway.

Bliss. To be freed again from lessons. A long train journey to Hannover, then through Hamlyn — are all the rats really dead now? — to Bad Pyrmont. The season was over. The chairs in front of the band stand had been stacked. The Palm Garden was deserted. I loved the stillness around me.

The Schillers were there. How did Gertrud and Senta manage to be excused from going to school, I wondered. But I did not ask. Uncle Schiller treated the old, lame and smelly dog who had been his companion in the aeroplane during the war, as if it was of even lower rank than his daughters who feared him. The poor creature was only allowed to hobble in the small study where Uncle Schiller's father usually sat in a leather armchair. Most of the time he was invisible because of the thick smoke erupting from his pipe.

Aunt Schiller was as gentle as ever. I cannot remember her ever having said a cross word. My mother thought the time had come to teach me how to wash myself and once, when my hands were not too clean after I had splashed them about in hot water, she smacked me. Unfortunately her wedding ring grazed my upper lip which started to bleed slightly.

"Look what you have done," I shouted, "you cut my LIP." I knew how to hurt my mother.

She made my lip bleed, not just any part of my face, but my lip. I was deliberately cruel and I don't think my mother

143

ever quite forgave me.

As usual I did not get on very well with Gertrud and Senta. Senta was too young for me and I did not want to play with her and Gertrud wanted to make all the decisions, where to go and what to do. Once when we were getting ready to get on a coach for an excursion, she made up her mind that it was she who should sit next to the coachman on the box. As I was a little older than her, I thought that I should have the privilege. After all, I was the guest. Bad Pyrmont was the Schiller's second home. Our argument finished up with Gertrud being slapped by her father. She was left behind.

The moving world was mine.

But I liked best to play by myself amidst the empty benches in front of the pump room, the leaves falling from the trees, rustling under my feet.

Suddenly some slow music came from the loudspeakers. Then there was an announcement. Somebody had died, somebody important. When I went back to the house, everybody was quiet and seemed depressed.

"This is the end of an era," said old Herr Schiller.

"Who died?" I asked father who had come for a visit.

"Stresemann. He was a great man. I don't know how much you know about the Weimar Republic, Martin, but Stresemann made it acceptable to the other nations."

"What will happen now?" asked my mother.

"Hitler must have been waiting for his death," said Uncle Schiller.

"Surely, the Nazis won't come to power?" asked Aunt Schiller.

"Of course not," replied Uncle Schiller.

"Nobody takes Hitler seriously," said father, "Hitler is a joke."

I left the room. The conversation of the grown-ups meant nothing to me.

*　　*　　*　　*

I have already said that I remember little of the long walk

during the night along the railway track, how later we spent the time in the morning while we were waiting for our friends to return from the town, where they were making inquiries about the possibility of us joining the army.

We could not have walked in silence all these hours? What did we talk about? Of course, we must have been down-hearted. Somebody had threatened to call the police. Another had pointed a gun at us. Did these two incidents make us abandon our original intention to find our way to the capital? Or perhaps something else happened, which I have forgotten, and which Paul did not record in his diary? Perhaps we had an argument amongst ourselves? Or we realised that it was impossible in the circumstances to reach Warsaw? Or did we feel that it was necessary for us to associate ourselves with the Polish cause in the war against the Germans?

We had very little money left. We were very hungry. But being hungry was not sufficient reason for wanting to join the army.

We had reason to hate the Germans, but did we? Can one hate what is part of oneself?

If Paul and I had been on our own, without our friends, the desire to join a group, any group, might have been too strong to resist — we knew what it meant to be isolated — but we were a quintet and could support each other. Franz's suggestion to find out whether we could enlist in a foreign legion — if such a 'legion' existed — was taken up by us all. Even Paul agreed, although he saw the danger to us, should we be captured by the Germans.

The major was 'found' by Rudi and Franz in the battered town. How did they find him? And who was this strange 'major' anyway? A major who was prepared to take a group of young people sixty kilometres to Lublin so that they could become soldiers. How did he know that there was a possibility of foreigners fighting the German army? How readily we handed over our papers, without which we had no proof that we were refugees from the Nazis. Without our papers we would be quite lost. Who would believe that we were Jews, caught up in the war and still hoping to get to England?

Everything sounds so incredible now. I should like to ask many questions. Why did we act in the way we did? There

145

are so many gaps which neither Paul nor I are able to fill.

At noon we shook hands with the major, a small man with glasses, dressed in civilian clothes, with a briefcase under his arm, where, we assumed our documents were kept. We started to walk, no more than a dozen of us, and felt safe for once. The heat was almost unbearable. We kept to the edge of the road, the overhanging branches of the trees gave some shade. A stream of horses, lorries packed with soldiers and other military traffic clattered and rumbled throwing up dust.

When the droning of planes could be heard, everything stopped and within a few seconds the stretch of road became empty of people. The string of animals and vehicles stood leaderless in disarray in the middle of the road. The men had taken shelter in the woodland beside the road. Sometimes there was the rattle of machine-guns, some of the planes flew very low. After the raid the road had to be cleared of damaged trucks and dead horses. There were many interruptions and our progress was slow.

Martin was content that there was somebody who was in charge. The major gave orders: "Take cover," or "Ten minutes resting," or "Forwards."

"How do you think, Paul, we shall manage being soldiers?"

"Don't ask me," replied Paul, "it's a crazy plan, but it would also have been crazy to try to make our way to Warsaw."

"The main thing is to survive."

"Why is surviving so important. I can think of worse things happening to us than dying."

"Our parents are waiting for us."

"I wonder whether they are. They must have given up all hope by now of ever seeing us again."

"We must do all we can to stay alive."

"Why must we? And in any case, it is not altogether up to us."

"I know that we shall see the parents again."

"You know? How do you know?"

"I know."

"Provided we are not gunned down by the Germans or the Poles."

"But the army will give us some protection."

"The army does not exist to give individuals protection. Where are the others, Martin? I can't see them."

"There they are. On the other side of the road, a hundred metres in front."

"Yes, I can see them now."

"I'm so thirsty, Paul. If we could only find some water."

"I am also thirsty."

"My throat is parched."

"You believe in miracles, Martin. Here is a pump. The water does not look too clean but it is water."

"Here's a tin, a bit rusty, but who cares. We could fill it up."

"We can't carry it while we are walking."

"Thirst is such a torture, Paul. I don't mind having so little to eat. But the heat, the dryness in my mouth — I can hardly speak — it's agony. How do you manage?"

"I am also thirsty all the time."

"But you can cope with your thirst. I can't. What is that over there?"

"Where?"

"On your right . . . a burnt out car. And on the grass . . . two people."

"They are dead, Martin. Probably killed by machine-guns."

"I have never seen a dead person before, Paul."

"Now you have seen two."

"They remind me of the puppets we had when we were small. After we played with them. When we put them away. Paul, these two were probably talking to each other an hour or two ago. And now they have become something we don't know anything about."

"They have become nothing."

"We don't know this. But there are so many killed in this war. How can I say that we shall be saved? I think we are going to come out of this all right. I think I know. But why should you and I be chosen and these two behind us not. I mean, have we got a right to hope?"

"You can always hope. It will not make much difference in the end."

"I'm frightened, Paul."

"We are both frightened. But one should not be afraid of death. There is certainly nothing frightening about a dead person. I have seen some. Dissection formed part of my medical studies, you know."

"What did you feel while you were dissecting?"

"You feel very little. There is a strong smell of formalin. When you are working you are only concerned with doing it properly. You are annoyed when there is too much fat or if you can't find an organ quickly enough. You are not aware that this body was once a person. It is just material, like any other material, preserved for you to practise on."

"And yet, Paul. These two dead soldiers. Perhaps they planned as we do. Perhaps they laughed and joked. You can't really believe there is nothing now, absolutely nothing. It is impossible, one moment there is, and then, all of a sudden, there is not."

"Where are the others, Martin?"

"I don't know. I can't see them now. They must be in front somewhere. We'd better run, Paul, and catch them up."

"I can't run any more, Martin."

"Neither can I."

"You could run, I'm sure, you could. Without me."

"Of course, I can't. I'm not Toni."

"Toni?"

"You remember Toni, my friend? He is one of those boys who can cope in every situation. If he had to run, he could and would overtake everybody. He could cope with thirst. With heat. Even with getting lost."

"Do you think we are lost?"

"We shall meet the others in Lublin."

"We won't make it today."

"They too won't be in Lublin before tomorrow. Anyhow, we won't lose our way."

"What makes you so sure?"

"I'm no Toni. But I have got a map."

148

"What map?"

"It belongs to Ernst. He dropped it where we had the soup this morning. I picked it up and forgot to give it back to him."

"We won't need it, Martin. This must be the main road to Lublin."

But the situation was more threatening than they thought. Here they were, walking on a main road used by the Polish military forces in broad daylight, two German-speaking young men with no documents to say who they were. When they realised this an hour or so later, they fell silent. Then they came to a crossroads, they did not know which way to turn. Martin did not dare to look at the map. There were no road signs. Paul's knowledge of Polish was too limited to risk asking somebody. Martin blamed himself for not memorising the map earlier when there were trees and bushes to hide in.

"I think we have to turn left," he said, "most of the traffic seems to go in this direction."

It was late afternoon and it was becoming a little cooler. They were both very tired and walking was becoming more and more difficult. They had to rest and settled down on the kerb. Here the road was wider and seemed even busier than previously. They watched the army trucks rumbling by, overfilled with singing soldiers. And horses. Hundreds of them. The smell of horses was sickly.

Dusk. Paul and Martin went on, slowly, wearily. They were exhausted and it was difficult for them to move. Then they heard the screeching of brakes somewhere near them. They did not turn round. They heard shouts coming in their direction but they did not think someone was addressing them. Two soldiers came up to them and spoke. The brothers shrugged their shoulders. The soldiers made them lift their arms and searched their pockets. They found the map. They had to get on the truck. Some rope was found and their hands were tied together.

"You . . . spies," a soldier said in German, "you carry a map of Poland. You are Germans."

"We are refugees," said Paul.
"That is what they all say," the soldier said.

Paul has described the ride in the lorry to Lublin as 'ghost-like'. Not because of the fear for our lives. Living was altogether too complicated anyhow. We were too weary to struggle on our own without our friends. Let our captors decide what to do with us. Perhaps we were even relieved that matters had been taken out of our hands. Or we were shocked, stunned, blunted. For once I did not feel like playing my special game of consequences. Our hands were tied together. Enough is enough. Why wish to go on living? There was nothing to live for.

The ride was ghost-like. The villages and towns we passed in darkness were lit up. Flames. Trees were aglow. Smoke bit into our eyes. Roofs were falling. People hurried, ant-like, carrying bits and pieces. Sounds of crackling wood, dropping bricks, flying glass. A burning village flitted away. It is already in the past. Another. Flames make their own pattern. A kind of terrifying beauty. Around us was unreality. A mild night breeze was fanning the fires. The burning stank. Trees waved their crowns in disbelief. The rumble of the trucks, the mauve sky lit, soldiers cowering like us, not comprehending like us. We gaped at the world which had lost its meaning. Paul and I were part of a scheme which could not be understood.

Let's leave it.

Let this be the end.

The end is already here.

God is burning.

We were interrogated in the Lublin Police Headquarters. They had untied us and pushed us into a room. There was a lamp hanging from the ceiling with a green metal shade. A senior officer with medals on his uniform bade us sit down. I looked at the lamp and thought it right that it had taken the place of the sun. There was no place for the sun any more.

Paul explained that he could understand some Polish but that his brother could only speak German. The officer replied in careful and slow German.

"You have been found with a map of Poland," he said.

He spoke gently and I thought that there were still fragments of this world which were healthy.

Paul told him how it happened.

"It is true we had a map on us. It is not ours but belongs to a friend. This friend is going with others to enlist with the foreign legion. A major is with them to help with the formalities."

It was too complicated to explain.

But the officer seemed satisfied.

"Can I see your identification papers?"

Paul replied that these were with the major.

"And where is this major of yours?"

Paul said that he did not know exactly. He was with the group on his way here to Lublin.

"Your story, although you must admit yourself it sounds somehow far-fetched, may be true. But we are at war. You are found on the road by our armed forces without papers but with a map. You are Germans. Germans. You will understand that we cannot let you go. I am sorry but we have no option. You will be dealt with in the morning according to the military law."

We understood that we would be executed the next day.

The small cell was overcrowded. Older and younger men, vagabonds (like the brothers) neglected and dirty (brothers of the brothers). There was only room to sit, to crouch down or to stand. There was irritated and excited talking. Paul and Martin had nothing to say to each other. There was nothing to say to the others who would anyway not understand them. It was best to keep silent. They had been told that something was going to happen to them in the morning, but this was as unreal as the burning landscape had been unreal.

One of the men spat, noisily and greedily. A fat blob of spittle splattered on the floor.

151

Martin found his voice. He was angry and disgusted.

"Stop it," he shouted in German, "stop it. Don't spit here. Don't."

Why should Martin care about somebody spitting? What did it matter? He, who would be spat out himself in a few hours time. He, who resembled the others, the tramps caked with filth, ridden with lice and with the looks of hungry animals. What was it that was talking? His background? His so-called middle-class upbringing? What impudence. Who did he think he was, that Jewish refugee, the outcast, rejected even by those who should be protecting him?

We have to teach him, haven't we, we have to teach this boy, full of self-importance and arrogance.

Or was there something else speaking? Some hope of survival, perhaps? Some trust in the unexpected happening?

Execution in the morning. Martin did not think of it, neither did Paul, who had smiled a little when he witnessed Martin lose his temper with the spitter, Martin who usually seemed to be so controlled, outwardly, at least.

I wonder what my thoughts were that night. Perhaps it is possible not to have any thoughts. Certainly, we did not much care what happened to us. Only the moment counted, nothing else. There was no point beyond it. We had reached a stage beyond fear.

As we lay huddled together covered with Paul's light coat, which we had used before as a cloak to shut out the world, I listened to Paul's breathing.

We were both exhausted. Sleep was a blessing.

The brothers were awakened by explosions, the familiar whistling of bombs, blasts and crashes. Paul and Martin stood up and leaned against each other. Then silence for a split second followed by a monstrous shriek. Crunching of wood, crashing of bricks. The walls of the cell showed deep cracks. Some of the men threw themselves against the cell door which was buckled. They shouted and screamed. They raged.

'Is this how people feel when they are buried alive?'

152

thought Martin. But neither he nor Paul took part in these outbursts of panic. Then the cell was unlocked. A warder shouted at them. The prisoners broke out. The brothers followed them. They stumbled through rubble. Disintegration around them. Wall and partitions had collapsed. Here and there instead of a ceiling there was the blueness of the sky. Furniture scorched or still burning stood in odd places, crackling and cackling like strange beasts. Files, folders and a thousand papers had become alive and tried to find a home somewhere.

Policemen stood erect in various corners, stunned. The officer who had interrogated the brothers the previous night, was carried away on a stretcher, blood oozing from his leg. Victory of chaos.

The brothers walked along the streets of Lublin, passing obscene scarred buildings. Towards somewhere. Where is somewhere? An open space. Trees and flower-beds singing their soundless songs unconcerned. A bench. A brown paper-bag. Bread. Some bread and butter. They settled down and ate. Sirens. The droning of planes. There was no reason to seek shelter. There was no reason to do anything.

After the raid they walked back to the police station and found someone to talk to. They did not let on that they had spent the night here. They asked where they could go now.

"Go and see a Jewish woman, they were told," she is well known for her welfare work. She might be able to suggest something."

The officer wrote down her address on a piece of paper.

The brothers asked passers-by and found the place where she lived. She was not unkind but she could not help.

"I'm just on my way to join my children," she said, "they live in a village a few miles from here. I'm sorry, but I can't take you with me."

She gave Paul some money. The brothers walked out of the town. A few kilometres further on they rolled into a ditch. They covered themselves with Paul's coat. They were able to sleep anywhere.

Anywhere was somewhere.

*   *   *   *

I often wondered what were the first words my mother spoke when she held me in her arms after the birth.

What did she feel when she saw that the baby was not perfect? Did she imagine that she had failed somehow? But how could the baby's ill-formed lip be her fault? Perhaps the doctor who attended her, reassured her: "These things happen. They cannot be foreseen."

Did my mother perhaps blame her husband who, she knew, had slept around even after he married her? She probably asked the doctor. "The baby's imperfection is due to a fault in the development of the foetus," the doctor must have replied.

"But why should this happen to me?" I can imagine my mother complaining, "why to me?"

The doctor no doubt comforted her: "You are not to blame."

And when my father entered the room, I can hear my mother saying to him almost angrily as if the result was his doing: "Look, Leo, look."

Father must have been shaken. "What can be done about it?"

The doctor explained.

"I know just the right man for this, a surgeon in Berlin. You can trust him absolutely. I shall get in touch with him straight away by 'phone. As soon as your wife is strong enough, you will both go with the baby to see him. The little boy needs to be operated on as soon as possible. Sucking will be difficult for him in the meantime."

Herr Rosen turned to his wife: "It does not matter all that much with a boy. A boy does not need to be beautiful."

"It is a strong child," said the doctor.

Frau Rosen wept. "Thousands of babies are born every day," she cried, "why must I give birth to a baby who is not perfect?"

"It is a lovely baby," said the doctor.

"All that is possible will be done for this child," said Herr Rosen, "even if we have to spend all the money we have."

Frau Rosen fell in love with the surgeon. She loved him for his distinguished looks — his sharp cut features, his greying hair, his steel blue eyes — but most of all, she loved him for his skill.

Very soon after the operation, the baby was able to take food like other babies. She loved him for being the master of the clinic, respected and even worshipped by his staff. She loved him for his love for his only child — he was a widower — she loved him also because he loved Beethoven as she did. She loved him because he was so unlike her husband whom she had never loved.

Professor Fried had to have his own way.

"Look here, Sarah," — they called each other by their first names almost immediately after the operation, "you can help me. There are babies here whose mothers can't feed them. You have got more milk than your little one needs. In fact, you are flowing over, my dear," and turning he called, "Nurse Eva, bring the little girl with the club-foot and the one whose fingers we operated on this morning."

Frau Rosen, putting the babies with some reluctance to her breasts, asked, almost in a whisper:

"Will there be enough for Martin?"

He reassured her and while feeding the babies she talked to him about her marriage and how she had nothing in common with her husband.

During the following years I was taken several times to Berlin for further surgical repairs. The friendship between my mother and Professor Fried deepened. He told her that if she was prepared to divorce her husband, he would ask her to marry him.

"Leo would never give up the children," my mother replied, "he is devoted to them both, especially to little Martin."

He bought a beautifully shaped glass jar with a brass top, which he had engraved with my mother's initials and his own intertwined.

Marriage was never mentioned again.

A garden full of sun. The baby in the pram looked up. A glittering object in the sky was caught in his bright, very blue eyes. Noisily the object disappeared. A different kind of noise was made by some boys rushing around him. His brother was amongst them. They ran into the house and back into the garden. The plane could still be heard in the distance. Now there was stillness. Only the bushes rustled. Suddenly the head of the brother appeared big over him. A large head with moving lips. Cooing sounds came from his mouth.

His brother was feeding him . . . more . . . more. But the baby could not swallow it, whatever it was. The baby moved his arms and kicked his legs and tried to cough and choked and gulped. He wanted to scream but he could not. Then he saw his mother's anxious face, heard her scream, heard his brother's scream, some newspaper was lying on the blue blanket in front of him. His mother cried out.

"What are you trying to do, Paul? Kill him? And his mouth, you know about his mouth. You devil you."

"He likes paper," screamed the four year old Paul, "he's hungry. He is always hungry. He's more important than I am."

A young woman in white ran towards them and picked up the baby.

"Where were you, Nanny?" — mother spoke sharply — "You are supposed to be with him. Not to chat indoors. Look at him. Look at his mouth, his poor mouth. Wash him quickly before infection sets in. Give him a bath."

Nanny took the baby into the house. His brother was being smacked. He heard his loud sobbing. Once more he could hear the rumbling plane and while Nanny undressed him he looked out of the window and stopped crying: things were falling from the sky, lots of them, little white shreds like leaves floating downwards.

Much later his brother came into the room, his eyes still red, holding a square piece of paper.

"This came from the heavens," little Paul explained,

"something is written on it. You can see it yourself," — and he held the sheet in front of the baby's eyes, "it says: baby is a stupid ugly baby." The baby started to cry. His brother bent over him and touched his cheek: "Never mind, baby," he said very gently, "never mind, I'll always look after you. I am your big brother."

The baby stopped crying. His brother went to the window and pressed his hot flushed face against the cool glass.

Bolle was the milkman. He dished out the milk from a large urn, which balanced like a large balloon in his cart, into white jugs which the waiting people had brought with them. Martin saw Bolle smiling at Lotte, the cook, and then Bolle was waving at him. Martin waved back. One of the first words Martin could say was 'Bolle'.

In Berlin the male nurse at the clinic wore a white coat like Bolle. "Bolle," said Martin to the nurse and he was given some milk in a cup. Bolle, the nurse, smiled at him the next morning and picked him up and carried him to a room which did not smell like milk, although it was white. Then Bolle, the nurse, pushed something into Martin's face and said: "Milk."

After the operation when Martin was back in his cot with burning swollen lips and a nasty taste in his mouth, he stammered — and only his mother could understand what he was saying:

"No Bolle . . . no more Bolle."

Little Martin was well formed, slender with long limbs, blue eyes, very fair hair, a small slightly bent nose like his father. But he did not look quite like other small children. His upper lip was heavily scarred.

"He will grow a moustache when he is grown up," his father said, "nobody will notice anything."

But it was a long time until then.

"Treat him like any other child," the paediatrician advised the parents.

Martin rocked to and fro when he was in bed. Asleep or awake, he rocked himself. Nobody understood why.

"You must stop him doing this," the paediatrician said.

Mother scolded him. Sometimes she pretended to smack him. She only hit the quilt.

"He will grow out of it," his father said.

But for many years Martin's head rocked from side to side.

"It helps me," Martin said when he was asked why he was doing it.

But nobody could understand that.

When Martin was invited to a children's party, his mother would dab face powder on his upper lip.

"Nobody will notice," his mother said but Martin knew otherwise.

Once there was a fancy dress party. His father, who was very clever with his hands, made a beautiful clown's mask. It was painted in bright colours. It covered Martin's whole face.

'Now nobody will know it's me,' Martin thought. But the other children wore masks which only covered their eyes.

He was easily recognised.

*　　*　　*　　*

The brothers crept out of the ditch. It was still very early, the sun had barely risen. Behind them Lublin was covered with smoke. They wondered whether they should return to the town and find out which road to take, but they did not want to report to the police again. There was just the chance that somebody might remember who they were. In any case, after the bombing by the Germans it was best to keep out of the Poles' way. But where to go? The map had been handed in. They had no papers. They were in the middle of nowhere with nowhere to go. Martin said that it was still best to get to Warsaw. One could report to the British Consulate there. The Consulate was bound to have some records and would know who they were. Then transport could be arranged.

"You are still convinced we can get to London?" asked Paul.

"Yes, I am," replied Martin.

"How many kilometres to Warsaw, d'you think?"

"I don't know. It's not really so important."

"Not important? What do you mean, it's not important to know how far we are away from Warsaw?"

"It's not a question of distance, of physical distance. But I know."

"You know what?"

"I know that we shall make it. That we shall get there."

"You still think we shall get to the parents?"

"I do, yes. I don't know how and when of course. But we shall see them. I know we shall."

"As we don't want to go back to Lublin, we might just as well go on."

"I think I remember from looking at the map, that Warsaw is north of Lublin. Certainly not south, more north-west."

"You and your map reading."

"Well, let's go on, anyway. We can always change direction when we see a sign post."

Indeed, after an hour's walk there was a sign post — Lubartow 12 km. "At least we know where the next police cell is going to be," said Paul.

The landscape was dry and flat.

Two slow-moving figures. Paul was holding his coat and Martin carried the little case, which had not been taken away from them. A case which contained a couple of dirty socks and soiled underwear.

"We could really throw away the case," said Paul, "we don't really need what's inside it."

"I would rather hang on to it. It makes me feel that we still have something which belongs to us," said Martin.

*   *   *   *

"Everything went wrong with that marriage from the start," said Paul, "there was mother, brought up strictly by her aunts, not beautiful, certainly, but attractive, educated as young girls were at the turn of the century, without knowing very much. She loved music and had probably read numerous romantic novels. She was not allowed much freedom. Chaperoned wherever she went. But she was not without talent,

159

Martin, you know. She had a pleasant singing voice – even now she can still sing – and I'm sure she was charming and vivacious. She went to concerts, to the theatre, to operas. Then she became stage struck. Did she ever tell you that she had an audition?"

"An audition?"

"Nikisch, Artur Nikisch auditioned her. His name won't mean anything to you, but he was a well known conductor many years ago. He advised mother to get training. I think she would have done very well as a light soprano in operettas. You can imagine her joy when she was told that she was good enough for the stage."

"But it was not to happen."

"No, of course not. Her parents would not hear of it. Their daughter on the stage? That was almost like having a daughter who wanted to become a prostitute. No, she was not allowed to have singing lessons."

"What a waste."

"It must have been a great blow to her. But then mother fell in love."

"But not with father, of course. I remember that one year, a long time ago, when we went for a walk with mother, she told you – I was not really supposed to listen – that she had never loved father. Father was thought by her parents to be a 'good match', the family Rosen was regarded as 'respectable'. The Rosens were fairly well-to-do and father was likely to become a manager of a large shop belonging to a chain, or something like that. But you know, although I had witnessed, as you did, many quarrels between the parents, it came as a great shock to me, hearing mother say that she had never loved father. Children seem to assume that parents love one another. I could not imagine that men and women marry and have children without love. Perhaps it was best I did not know. I don't think I could have borne it."

"Mother fell in love with a chemist when she was still in her teens. According to her, he was a highly cultured man. Strong but gentle. Interested in the things mother was interested in, particularly music. Yes, they wanted to get married. But mother's parents said no. Once again, no. Mother was near a nervous breakdown, she told me. Jubilant one moment, depressed and utterly dejected the next. When someone suggested good-looking Leo Rosen would make a perfect match, mother agreed, if only to get away from home. Her own mother had been very ill for a long time. When mother was a young girl she was looked after by three well meaning but narrow-minded aunts who made life hell for her."

"So they got married."

"So they got married. And things started off badly, when they were on their honeymoon. Mother knew nothing about sexual matters. Many women didn't in those days. The initiation into love-making was left to the husbands. Our father was no doubt experienced in these matters. But mother told me that consummation was not possible for some reason. When they came back from Italy, father asked some friends for advice and was told to force himself into the body of his wife. This he told me himself a couple of years ago — no doubt, he felt, that as a medical student I should know about such things. The next evening he gave mother a lot of wine to drink. And then he practically raped her. 'What was I to do?' he said to me, 'I did not know any better, this is what I was told to do. And your mother too thought it was best to take the bull by its horns and get it over with.' And she bled and bled. There was a moment when father thought she was going to bleed to death. And that was the start of their marriage."

"How is it, that they kept together all these years, Paul?"

"It is because of us, you and me. Neither would have been prepared to give us up. Father always felt particularly close to you — oh, I know it's difficult for you to make contact with him, but this does not alter the fact that he is very attached to you. Mother made me into a substitute husband."

"What do you mean, 'substitute husband'?"

"For mother, I am what father is not. Reliable, clever, interested in the things she is interested in, no dreamer, as sceptical as she is herself. So she treated me since I was little, not as a son but as an intimate friend. This has been and still is a burden, Martin. It is not easy to explain, she has tied me to her, we are knotted together. Whenever I spoke to a girl, it was as if she stood next to me and looked at both of us disapprovingly. I don't think she can bear the possibility

161

that I should fall in love. We have never talked about it, Martin, I am attracted to beautiful women, but in the end I shrink back. Mother does not know this, of course, but it is she who stops me from getting close, really close to women. I love and adore from a distance, so to speak, but then I fail them, again and again, I fail. Mother wants me to fail. I must break away from mother. I love her and want to be with her. But I must break away. I cannot live and love, with her at my side."

"You Paul, and mother. Father and I. I always knew he wanted me to be like him. But I am not like him. A dreamer, yes. But I am not interested in the things he is interested in: he knows I write poems but he does not take me seriously. He said to me once: 'writing poems does not get you anywhere'."

"And yet you have much in common."

"How?"

"Well, looks for one thing. You look like father, I, like mother. And then there is something of father in you. He too is a kind of artist. If things had turned out differently for him, perhaps he could have used his creative gifts as you are using yours. But now he just dreams, dreams of success, riches . . ."

"I'm also a dreamer, I know."

"You dream of being united with the parents."

"This is not a dream, Paul. It doesn't feel like a dream. It's something which tells me we shall see the parents."

"It just shows you how close you are to them."

"I think we are both very close to them."

They arrived at Lubartow in the early afternoon. Here, nothing had been destroyed. Houses undamaged, gardens spread with flowers, trees heavy with apples and plums. There was even a smell of cooking. But there were not many people about. There were a few old women, too warmly dressed in this heat, their hair covered with black or brown shawls, a bearded Jew in his ancient outfit. Nobody took any notice of the two intruders who obviously came from strange lands and did not fit in.

Paul and Martin were hungry. Hunger had not worried them too much until now. They had spent a little money on food or they had been given some. It was thirst which was more of a problem, Martin particularly suffered from the lack of water. Thirst he found unbearable and any well, pump or tap they found was like a precious gift. But now they were both hungry. None of the shops seemed to be open. As in other places they had come through, the doors were locked and the windows barricaded or the shutters closed. There was deadness in the streets.

But they saw a woman bending over the garden fence, looking at them slyly and with a little curiosity. She called them, shouting in Yiddish, which the brothers could understand.

"No one here. All gone. Gone."

They walked across to her. Her face was crumpled and mask-like. Only her eyes were alive.

Martin said that they wanted some food.

"Nothing to eat. Everybody gone away. Away from here. Most of them. Bad times. Such bad times. The Germans are coming."

"We are Jews from Germany," said Paul, "refugees from the Nazis."

"German Jews?" she replied harshly, "and have you helped the Polish Jews when they needed help? German Jews, no Jews. They think they are cleaner, more clever than us. They made money. Lots of money. German Jews are Germans, not Jews. When we came across the border, they spat at us. We asked for help, they said we were dirty. You are Germans. You speak German not Yiddish. How do I know you are Jews? You don't look like Jews. You look like Goyim. Goyim despise us. You despise us. We are not good enough for you. You have had your lesson now. Hitler had to tell you. He told you, you are Jews. You didn't know before, did you? Now you come to us. Now. Now you need us. When we came to you, you gave nothing. Nothing. Now you want. But we have nothing to give. Nothing to give you."

Her long speech had exhausted her. The boys did not understand all she had screamed out. But they had understood her anger. Martin thought 'The Germans. The Poles. And now the Jews. Everybody hates us.'

Paul, using a mixture of German, Czech and Yiddish tried to explain that all this had not been their fault, they were young and had never looked down on a Polish Jew. He did not tell her that they had rarely ever seen a Polish Jew in Germany, wearing a caftan and a felt hat, and that they had never heard anyone in Breslau speaking the ghetto language. Martin wanted to get away, get away from her. She was so full of indignation and anger and there was nothing one could say in one's defence.

*　　*　　*　　*

When he was a boy, his mother transformed his room once a year, into an old clothes' shop: all the worn out pants and vests and socks and the shirts which Paul and Martin had outgrown, and sheets too thin to be mended, and towels, faded and often threadbare, and shoes which had become too tight or too ugly, and suits, his and Paul's and father's and grandfather's, which had become unsightly or outmoded or could not be repaired, and dresses of his mother's to which she had taken a dislike, and other bits and pieces, cloth, material, netting, curtains, cardigans with holes, frayed pullovers which had lost their colour, but also other trinkets, nothing to dress in but things to look at, which had been hidden in some dark corner in the flat because they were too ugly, or chipped vases and bowls, china dogs, perhaps a clock with the hour-hand missing or a broken watch.

All this worthless junk had been carefully laid out in the room, in little heaps on the chairs and on the bed and on the floor, awaiting Frau Seeliger who came annually across the border from Poland to Breslau to buy discarded things from Jewish families. Frau Seeliger was a tiny woman, wrapped up in a tight garment and wearing high boots with laces. She spoke German and Yiddish, jumbled up. She was no fool. She maintained that she paid the best prices anyone would pay for all that trash. She was a good judge of quality and little Martin was fascinated, watching her dancing around the room, shaking her small head in disbelief, haggling,

164

using her bony arms and expressive hands and fingers, on the way out — "I can't sell any of this rubbish, throw it away, Frau, I don't want it," — returns, feels, clicks with her tongue, raises her eyebrows and says: "I give you fifty marks for the lot. And good riddance. But if you have a dinner suit, that is good, that is wanted. I give you a good price for a dinner suit."

Frau Rosen said that she did not have a dinner suit, but fifty marks was a ridiculous offer, even she, Frau Seeliger, must see that, that green dressing-gown over there, practically unworn, was alone worth ten marks. Martin knew his mother was lying.

Then mother brought some more stuff which she had kept in reserve and Frau Seeliger, of course, had expected this. Finally a price was agreed, mother's pocket money, enough to buy something useless, Martin thought.

And with a slight, almost imperceptible shuddering, Frau Rosen would shake hands with Frau Seeliger and ask her to stay for a cup of coffee (knowing this would be refused).

"You will come next year?" Frau Rosen asked, "I might be able to let you have my husband's dinner suit."

"Dinner suits I always take," said Frau Seeliger.

Everything was being bundled up and left in the entrance hall.

"My son will collect," Frau Seeliger said.

And when she had left, Frau Rosen asked the maid to open all the windows.

"That woman smells," she said.

Martin guessed that the smell was the smell of old clothes.

*   *   *   *

Paul and Martin turned away from the woman who stood behind the gate. But she shouted after them: "Come," and then, "Wait," and a few minutes later she came back from the house with something wrapped up in newspaper.

"Take," she said and when Paul tried to thank her she interrupted him: "Where you go?"

"Warsaw," Paul replied.

"Warsaw — a long way," she said and went back into the

house.

They started to eat the bread and the sausage while walking and stuffed the raw potatoes, on which still clung some dark soil, into their pockets. When they had left Lubartow behind them, they wanted to cook the potatoes but, of course, they had no matches to light a fire.

"Can one eat potatoes raw?" asked Martin.

"I don't know. We'll keep them for an emergency."

The bulbous objects in their pockets gave some feeling of security. A policeman was waiting for them in the middle of the road. He ordered them to accompany him back to Lubartow.

As they entered the little town once more — this time from the other end — they noticed a small group of people walking towards them. Martin recognised Blau, the committee chairman and two other members. He was overjoyed.

'We are not on our own,' he thought, and he wanted to call out. But Paul gave him a gentle push. The group did not wish to be recognised. 'Even friends are turning into strangers,' Martin thought.

A little later Paul said, "Perhaps it was not such a good idea after all, for Blau to take us into the train."

Martin had no answer ready.

"We'd better stick to the story that we want to join the foreign army group," said Paul, "they won't accept that we want to get to the capital."

Once again they were being questioned. Again they stood in front of a desk behind which there was someone who tried to understand Paul's confused explanations in broken Czech and German.

Suddenly there was a roar of a plane, the man behind the desk jumped up from his chair as if stung and pulled off the rifle which was hanging on a hook behind him. He ran outside, the noise of the low-flying plane was almost unbearable. Then they heard a few shots, the noise became weaker and weaker and then there was silence at last, Martin prayed for the plane not to return.

The officer came back into the room and wordless he opened the door again and indicated the brothers were to leave.

But they did not walk for long.

"What is the point of trying to get to Warsaw," said Paul. "We'll never make it anyhow. It's crazy to go on. We don't know where the German army is. They could have occupied the capital by now."

"We have not seen any Germans and Warsaw is further north," said Martin.

"Your knowledge, Martin, of military matters is somewhat limited. Armies make a habit of coming from different directions."

"Well, what do you suggest?"

"It's only the police that can help us."

But the police did not. When they reported again at the Lubartow Police Station, the officer probably thought he was dealing with mentally deranged characters. The brothers were taken to a cell with a large wooden platform along the wall and thick bars outside the window which looked into the street.

There were others here.

Martin went to the window.

There was a tree in the distance, slightly swaying its branches. He could also see a patch of blue.

"At least one has not got the feeling one is walled in," he said to Paul, "this is more like a room than a cell."

"I can think of a more comfortable room," said Paul.

"It's certainly an improvement on the cell in Lublin."

"Well, they have not threatened to kill us."

But Martin's momentary feelings of relief gave way to a feeling of hopelessness which he did not want to share with Paul. 'Is this torment never going to end?' he thought, 'there is, of course, no chance of reaching Warsaw. And how can we join the army without papers? Who will believe our story if we are unable to prove who we are?'

"It's not so bad here, Paul," he said and Paul shrugged his shoulders.

'We are already lost,' Martin thought, 'losing our lives would be no more than confirmation. An end. The conclusion of an unheroic episode. If only we had learnt something from the week when we crossed the border. It was a kind of rehearsal: the desolation, the despair, the inability to act.

But we have not grown from it, we can't use that experience, we can't rise above it, we are caught, caught again in a net from which we can't disentangle ourselves. If we could only say 'yes here we are,' and smile a bit, and do what we can to save ourselves, but we are so feeble, so rejecting, so agonised and torn to pieces as if we had willingly thrown ourselves away. Of course, I'm not convinced we shall survive. How can I be convinced. I know nothing else but to say to Paul: we shall make it, we shall make it. How real is my stubborn refusal to admit defeat, how real my belief in this God, our leader in this desert? I have no close contact with Him, no direct line to Him. The voice inside me is my voice, not HIS. Why should Paul and I come out of this safely, when so many must die. I shall not pretend any more. I shall tell him that I believe we won't make it. We are not fit to make it. We failed. We failed.'

There were only a few men sharing the cell and they kept to themselves and did not ask any questions. The brothers walked up and down the cell or stood by the window or lay on the platform.

In one corner was a large pail of urine, around which fat flies buzzed. There were many flies in the cell. The men shook their heads like horses.

"I was thinking of grandfather," said Paul, "I wonder how he is, now Germany is at war."

"The Nazis have got enough on their hands. They don't bother about the Jews."

"I felt bad that we had to emigrate without him, Martin. I know it would not have been possible — he was nearly seventy-five, wasn't he? — and yet to have to leave him behind."

"Of course, the parents wanted him to follow us."

"If any of father's plan had materialised, yes. But everything was so vague, father's schemes were so wild."

"But Paul, he did believe at the time that things would work out all right. I'm sure he was convinced."

"Perhaps he was convinced. It is pointless to talk about it now. Grandfather must have missed us so much. After all, he had lived with us for as long as I can remember."

"I don't think he blamed the parents."

"He wasn't the easiest of persons to live with, Martin, I know. He often gave mother a bad time. He was very fond of father."

"I think they liked each other. It was a friendship."

"Mother could never forgive him for stopping her going on the stage or for not allowing her to marry the man she loved."

"He was a bit of a tyrant, wasn't he?"

"Oh, I agree, he was. And yet, I have a lot to thank him for. He was very important to me when I was a child. Not only because he was always around the house. He respected me as a person, he made no demands on me, but was interested in everything I did."

"He did not care that much about *me*, Paul."

"You were too young for him. He probably felt he was too old to start all over again, when you arrived on the scene. He was impatient with me, I remember, when I was small. But when I was older he could relate to me and I to him."

"He had few friends. There were the Goldsteins to whom he went every Tuesday night to play cards and the cigar merchant Joseph — you remember him? He had a huge wart on one of his cheeks which fascinated me — but he didn't see him often."

"And Aunt Minna, of course."

"I don't think he liked Aunt Minna very much, although she was his closest relative, except for mother."

"How he played up mother sometimes. Those angina attacks. Whenever she had said something he didn't approve of, or when she got ready to go out for the evening, he had one of those attacks."

"You think he pretended to have them, Paul?"

"I don't know about pretending. He wanted to upset mother, delay her departure from the house, punish her in some way. His body did what his mind asked it to do."

"It was terrifying watching him when he had those attacks. It was as if he was suffocating."

169

"Well that is what it feels like."

"But then the tablets he had, they worked like a miracle."

"Nitroglycerin. He had to chew them, not swallow them."

"Paul, I suffered with him when I saw him in such pain and gasping."

"He wanted to make mother suffer, not you. He and mother felt very little for each other. But do you remember the woman who did his washing?"

"I do. I could never understand why his laundry was not done with ours by the washerwoman who came every fortnight."

"Well this is a bit of a mystery. She was quite a beautiful woman, plump with a sweet open face."

"Why, Paul, do you think, there was something between them?"

"I think mother suspected something. Why should he have his things washed separately? And there was once a terrible row between mother and him because of the expensive presents he gave to that woman. It's possible they had an affair when he was younger. And that young man . . ."

"You mean the lad who collected and brought the laundry?"

"Didn't you think he looked a little like grandfather?"

"Looked like him?"

"I wonder whether he was grandfather's son."

"Just imagine — he could have been mother's half brother. Is it really possible?"

"Well, Martin, we shall never know."

"I never thought much about grandfather after we left. He was too often cross with me. When I played with children in the street outside the house he shouted out of the window because of the noise. He could not control his anger. When he thought I was naughty he threatened to tell mother. He spent so much time with you, Paul, that he had none left for me. When I rocked in bed, he frightened me by shouting at me. And yet when there was a thunderstorm he allowed me to slip into his bed. And I felt for him when he warmed his cold hands on the mug of hot caffeine-free coffee which mother insisted he had instead of real coffee which was not good for his health. And I felt for him when he was told to keep out of the way when guests arrived. But I was able to show him that I was on his side. We came closest when I accompanied him to the cemetery. Every week he went to tend the grave of the grandmother we never knew. Every week. Miles from where we lived. Only father could stop him from going when the weather was very bad. I enjoyed going with him. In the tram he let me have his walking stick which I wedged between my thighs. I pretended to be the tram driver, turning the crook in all directions. And then the short walk to the grave. I liked the sound the trees made, sounds which did not disturb the stillness around me. I felt small but there was a strange kind of contentment. How he must have loved his wife. He always talked about her on these Sunday mornings: about her goodness, her gentleness and how he still missed her and often tears came into his eyes when he sat on the little bench next to the stone and looked at the white chrysanthemums which he had planted."

"This did not prevent him from being unkind to his daughter on so many occasions."

"We all have many faces, Paul."

The next morning, while Paul helped the other prisoners to scrub the floor of the cell, Martin carried the bucket, full to the brim, to the yard at the back, emptied it and washed it out with some sharp disinfectant. Martin was surprised that he could do this without feeling nauseated.

'Perhaps I love people after all,' he thought, 'in spite of what they are doing to each other and to Paul and to me.'

Later he went to the window and looked at the empty street, the bars cut it into sections, but the branches of the tree at the back could not be stemmed, they grew through the obstacles.

Then Martin saw the other three of the quintet. At least he thought he saw them. There were Rudi and Ernst, Franz was walking a little behind, as usual. They did not talk to each other and plodded along slowly. Martin shouted:

"Rudi . . . we are here."

171

But if they *were* there, they could not possibly have heard him. The men in the cell turned to Martin. Paul ran to him and put a hand on his shoulder.

"I saw them, Paul, I saw them. I'm telling you, the others went by. But they didn't see me or hear me."

"Perhaps you saw them because you wanted to," said Paul. Martin dropped his head, "You don't believe me."

"It's very unlikely. They have joined the army, don't you remember? The last time we set eyes on them was sixty, seventy kilometres from here. You must be mistaken. Delusions are caused by lack of food."

"They seemed so real, Paul, as real as you, standing next to me. But why should they come this way? I can see that. I must have imagined it."

The next day the brothers stood once again, the third time, in front of the desk. The officer — whose rifle hung on the wall like a sculpture displayed for show — looked at them for a long time and then handed them their papers, two German passports and the two notifications from the British Consulate which stated that Paul and Martin Rosen were refugees from Nazi oppression.

The officer explained that three young men had called the previous day and left the documents. Apparently they were on their way to Lemberg.

Paul and Martin walked out of the police station, dazed.

"And where is Lemberg?"

"It is south-east from here, I think."

"It's not anywhere on the way to Warsaw?"

"It must be in the opposite direction."

"How far do you think it is to walk?"

"How am I to know?"

"Do you think we can catch up with the others?"

"I doubt it."

"But we might meet them in Lemberg."

"Perhaps."

"Let's walk to Lemberg."

After walking a few kilometres, Martin said: "Why are we going to Lemberg? From Warsaw we might be able to get away. We know nothing about Lemberg. We don't even know where it is. I have some idea it is near the Romanian border."

"Perhaps they want to cross the border there."

"If it's further than Warsaw, and I think it well might be, then we are not going to make it, Paul."

"What do you suggest?"

"I think we should go back to Lubartow and do what we originally planned, go to Warsaw."

"At least we have got our identification papers now."

It was almost night when they entered the town once more. It was strange to see a small group of people standing in front of a low building.

"We hardly saw anybody all day long. Where do these people come from?" asked Martin.

"Everything is like a fantasy," said Paul. "A painful fantasy. If we could only glide along, like fish, in and out without thought, take shelter here and there, in a cavity, behind some rocks, slithering along, soundless, in complete silence, existing without insisting, the fantasy could be bearable."

They entered the building, a kind of hostel. There were no beds available. But they were not sent away. They pushed two tables together and covering themselves with Paul's coat, their heads touching in the warm darkness, they saw and heard nothing in spite of the commotion in the room.

Early next morning they were on their way again and followed the road they had taken a few days before. After two hours they came to a crossroad. There were no signposts. It could be the road in front, which led to the capital, or the road to the right, or the road to the left. They decided to ignore the turnings. But after a few hundred metres they returned to the crossing. Perhaps one should take the left turning after all. Martin tried to visualise the map which had been lost. They took the left turning but when they heard the barking of a dog they halted and went slowly back to where the road divided and sat at the edge of the road which had taken them there.

"We might just as well turn right," said Paul, "it doesn't seem to make any difference which way we go."

"If we are meant to get there, it doesn't matter which road we take," said Martin.

"That sounds like one of the pronouncements of the Delphian oracle. These could also be interpreted just as you wished," replied Paul with some bitterness.

"I'm not an oracle, Paul. I feel as hopeless as you do."

"So you're not convinced any more, that we shall succeed in getting to England?"

"I am not convinced, no. How can I be convinced?"

"But?"

"It's not a question of conviction. It's a matter of faith."

"If you believe, then you are convinced."

"But it's not as simple as that. If I think rationally, I can't be convinced that we'll survive without skills, food and all the other things which are necessary for such an odd journey. No, I can't be convinced that we'll cope in our present situation, two German Jews in Poland, a Poland which has always hated Jews and is now at war with Germans from whom we've already fled twice. I'm not mad, Paul, not mad yet. The madness is happening around me, not inside me. I know as well as you do, that we really have little chance of getting out of this mess. But in spite of everything, oh, I know how ridiculous this must sound, I feel we're being led. In spite of a hundred doubts, I can't help sensing that we are driven on, and that we are submitting ourselves to whatever is driving us forward or backward, like leaves from trees and bushes which are swept in all directions as if there was some purpose. Perhaps it will all end differently to what we're hoping. It's possible that something we can't imagine is in store for us. But I can't believe that everything is pointless. Pointlessness is such a waste and I can't believe there is such waste in life, I mean waste of *our* lives, Paul. I hardly understand what I am talking about. In an hour I shall probably deny what I've said just now. I'm so weak, you know that, I've always been weak. I say something and I think it's true and a little later I'm not certain any more. I can't think things through. Perhaps I'm not all that bright, I know. And then I'm inconsistent, I'm so inconsistent, always swaying, never still, and always so full of doubts. Why should I know more about life and belief than you do?

174

I'm just talking, talking, talking . . . ''

Martin was almost crying.

After a while Paul said quietly, "But if everything is pre-ordained, as you say, we might just as well not go any further. We might stop by this tree stump and wait for death. This would be as logical or illogical as going on in this wilderness."

"But we don't stop, Paul. We won't. We have now taken the right turning. The right turning. Even if it turns out to be the wrong one, you understand Paul, it is the right one for us."

"The road to the parents?"

"The right road for us . . . yes, I believe we shall see them," but doubt had crept into Martin's voice.

A little way from the road a blueish vapour curled into the sky. Two men were sitting near a fire. One of them whistled and the brothers stopped and then went into the field towards them. Paul said something to the men and Martin was again surprised how well Paul managed to make himself understood with his limited knowledge of Czech. The brothers were asked to sit down with the men. They handed over the potatoes which they had kept in their pockets. These were placed into the hot white ashes.

'Who are these two,' Martin asked himself, 'where do they come from and where are they going? Are they like us, escaping from something? But they don't look like refugees.'

Paul said: "They say the road is free."

"What do they mean by the road is free?"

"This is the road to Warsaw. They say one can get through. There are no armies. They say we should go on."

'They seem to know,' Martin thought, 'they are so resourceful, they have got matches or know how to make a fire without matches, they got themselves a tin to boil water, and where did they get the water from? It smells like chicken soup. Where did they get the chicken from? And now one man takes from his rucksack four bowls and four spoons. They are cooking for us, for us who know nothing and can do nothing, for us who are wallowing in our distress.'

After the meal when the brothers had thanked them and got ready to start walking, Paul with his coat, the comfort cloak, over his arm and Martin clutching the little case with the useless dirty pieces inside, the two men spoke to Paul.

"They say we should rest until tomorrow, there's no hurry," Paul said to Martin.

"What do they mean, there is no hurry?"

Paul shrugged his shoulders.

"They say we are too exhausted. They are against further walking today. We should stay with them. They know of some shelter for the night, we could all sleep there together."

'Who are these two?' Martin thought, 'they are taking us over. We are nothing but clay in their hands.'

"I don't think we can refuse their offer," said Paul.

'They will not hurt us,' thought Martin, 'I know they won't.'

Then the four of them crossed the field. There was a gap amongst the thick hedges at the far end which stood up like a green wall. They came to a large shed, more like a coach house. It was quite empty inside apart from some sacks lying in a heap in a corner. Martin, looking around him, could hardly believe his eyes: there was a tap sticking out of the wall and a small puddle on the stone floor. He ran to it and turned the tap: water, cold, clear, holy. He put his head under the stream, and let the water run down his face, drinking, splashing, drinking, jubilating, drinking. Then he turned round to Paul who stood behind him and shouted:

"A kind of baptism."

"We could still leave them, if you like," said Paul.

Martin only shook his head.

Some time during the night, Paul woke Martin.

"I must go outside," he said, "I shan't be long."

'This is the first time we are not together,' Martin thought. He wanted to go after Paul to find out what was wrong, but he did not want to disturb the others who were sleeping a

176

short distance away from the brothers. He prayed for Paul's return.

"Diarrhoea," whispered Paul when he stretched out next to Martin under the coat. It was the beginning of Paul's illness, which was to last for many days.

*   *   *   *

We were walking through a nebulous world but even now, more than forty years later, the fog is thickening. I should be able to remember more than I do. I know I have not told everything, there are so many gaps. A day is long. There are so many hours from dawn to dusk. How did we fill them? Certainly, we must have talked a lot to each other, about ourselves, about the parents about our childhood. We always looked for water or for food. Sleep was important. Huddled together, covered with Paul's coat, our agonies often became pliable, bearable, sometimes even acceptable. But there must have been more to the day than I can now narrate. I know that I avoided looking at the landscape and I cannot therefore describe it. Everything seemed covered with some kind of hot grey dust, nothing hung together, no beautiful slopes, no hillsides, no views. It could not have been so, of course, but I shut it all out because I could not have borne it. Nature had conspired against me. No help would come from the trees, the grass, the flowers, the birds. It could give no solace. On the contrary, nature stood outside as if to say: you suffer without me, what you have to go through, you go through without me. What you have loved before, was part of you and that you have lost. What you have observed is now observing you.

Was our behaviour 'normal'? Is it not incredible that we seemed to be drawn to the places and situations where there was most danger? The bomb blast in Lublin. Imprisoned because of suspected spying in war time. The prison is destroyed, only the cell remains intact. In the following chaos we were released. Did it really happen? If it were not for Paul's diary, I would doubt my own memory. We returned to the police headquarters as if we were asking to be dealt with, now that the raid was over. Then Lubartow. Going

177

back to the police station, almost demanding to be put into a cell. What made us go back to our captors? Perhaps it was the human voice, the father and mother we were seeking and seeing in anyone who was directing us. It is difficult to discuss our conduct, our unreasonable conduct. But other strange happenings crossed our path. The ghost-like appearance of our friends. Why did they come to Lubartow? Were they looking for us? Presumably the 'major' had returned our papers to them, when it became clear that there was no army group one could join. But were our friends actually looking for us? And how could they possibly have known where we were? Lubartow is an unimportant town − it is not even mentioned in the Polish Travel Guide − there must be dozens like it within a radius of twenty-five kilometres of Lublin. Why did they come this way? If they were on their way to Lemberg, they were walking in the opposite direction. Did they make enquiries in each place they passed? But asking for two young foreigners, being foreigners themselves, would have been foolish, surely dangerous to themselves. Did they hear me when I called out from the cell? Perhaps they did. But why didn't they make a sign to show us that they knew where we were? After our discharge from imprisonment, we could not make up our minds which way to go. We still wanted to get to Warsaw. But, of course, we did not know then that the Germans had already practically surrounded the capital, and we would not have been able to reach it anyway. For us, the possibility of being put on a plane to England still existed. There *was* a solution, we thought, a solution we had to find in spite of the lack of clues. Going backward and forward, left and right: one road must lead us to the capital. At the crossroads we finally decided. And according to the two men who had invited us for a meal which they had prepared, it was the right decision. The road was free, whatever that meant. We accepted their judgement. They frightened me. I was frightened by their concern for us. Two compassionate men in the wilderness. I was like one of the shepherds in the song, for mighty dread had seized my troubled mind when I saw the angels.

In spite of Paul's illness — it turned out to be some form of dysentery — we made good headway the following day. Once more we were members of a group, the two men walked with us. We felt protected. In two or three days, we thought, we would reach Warsaw. Now that we had our papers returned to us, now that we were going in the right direction, our hopes had risen.

Outside Lukow, something was going on. Soldiers and civilians were rushing about. At first we could not make out the cause of such hectic activity. Some people stood in the street and looked up into the tops of trees. There was almost an air of festivity, something domestic, holiday-like, an atmosphere of normality which evoked memories. People laughed, jostled each other, chatted to one another. Someone ran. Another shouted. There were some apples on the ground. Then the whistle of a policeman. A boy jumped on a bicycle. His pockets bulged. The policeman stood helpless, two fists at his hips. The raid on the fruit trees continued. Nobody took any notice of him. Perhaps he did not want to catch the thieves. More apples rained, were gathered up as soon as they hit the ground. Some children caught them in mid-air. More people seemed to arrive on the scene. There was another policeman. He started to climb the tree and was made fun of by the crowd. Soon he gave up. And then, suddenly all was still. It was as if the film director had shouted, "Cut". Paul and I and the two men, we, the audience looked at each other and started to laugh. It was like the end of a funny film. The street was empty. Suddenly the men shook our hands. They could not come with us. They pointed with their hands in the direction we should take. It was as if someone had called them away. 'Perhaps there are others who need them,' I thought.

The fun around the fruit trees had left behind in the brothers a sensation of gaiety.

"If people can behave so frivolously, perhaps all is not lost," said Paul.

"It was as if they wanted some sport on a sunny afternoon. Perhaps they had forgotten about the war."

"Do you remember the occasion when I came to visit you in Brünn last winter and we danced in the snow on the way back from the cinema?"

"We saw a film by the Marx Brothers."

"It was not the film which made us behave in such a wild manner."

"Still, it was a very funny film. All those people trying to get into that tiny cabin on the boat."

"It was a moment of release for us, Martin. Release from the deep depression we all suffered. The gloomy mood at home with the parents was almost too much to bear. We expected Hitler to march in any day."

"I felt so sorry for father. Even he had lost hope of getting us away from Czechoslovakia in time. We know so little about him. He never talks about himself, does he? He lives a life he does not want to share."

"I don't think he *can* share it. Not in the way you would like him to. He's like an artist who, only through what he creates, can open the door to himself."

"Father is no artist, Paul."

"No, he does not write poetry or make music or paint pictures. This is his tragedy. This he shares with those who have no means of expressing what they would like to express. That's why he keeps to himself and only lets us see what he thinks we would like to see."

"But he doesn't succeed in anything."

"He fails. Again and again he fails. He failed as a businessman, a husband, a provider for his family. He even failed as a father, a father to me, at least."

"Because he did not share your interests?"

"No, Martin. Interests don't matter all that much. But he knew that mother had taken on his role as far as I was concerned. As he hadn't anything to give her, perhaps he felt he couldn't take me away from her. He abrogated. Therefore he failed. Perhaps I am wrong. Things are never simple and father is no simple person. When you were small he was probably determined not to let you go. He had lost one son, he did not want to lose another."

"But he lost me too."

"He is very attached to you."

180

"Yes, I know. But we have got nothing to say to each other."

"You are not the son he hoped you would be. Like him, you have shut yourself away."

"I would like to have a different father, a stronger father to whom I could look up."

"We all want different parents."

"I needed him when I was little. At least I had you."

"Even his attempt to reach you came to nothing."

"And somehow it should not have been so difficult for him. I felt close to him when he told us about his childhood in Reisen, the little old town which I always associated with the dark ages, I don't know why. You remember, there was a palace he often mentioned, a real palace with a real Count. And the quaint market square with the gabled houses and the shop of our grandfather. He sold oil and grain and stuff for the farmers, didn't he? And grandfather, that old tyrant, was regarded in high esteem by many people who came to him for advice about property and other money matters. There was a watchmaker in the town who admitted to father that he kept watches handed in to him for repair for several extra weeks. How could he justify charging his customers a Taler or two, if the repaired watch was returned within a week? And there was the mentally defective boy who was not only accepted by the community but loved for his simplicity. Or the scandal about the threatening letters written anonymously. They found out who wrote them by marking all the envelopes which were sold locally. Or father's games by the river when he was a child. Or father's mother, whom we never saw, apparently slaving willingly for the very large family headed by Grandfather Rosen, counsellor and autocrat and highly respected Jew."

"We went to see him once or twice when he lived in Breslau. An odd, querulous old man."

"I was very little then. But I remember he was looked after by a male nurse who made model boats out of tree bark."

"You can still remember that, Martin?"

"And do you remember about that strange document which grandmother Rosen had to sign?"

"What document?"

"Father told us that grandmother Rosen had to promise not to die before her husband. A document to this effect was drawn up by a solicitor and grandmother's signature was witnessed. Grandfather Rosen never forgave his wife for breaking her promise."

"I don't believe that story, Martin. It's too crazy. But how burdened we all are with the burden of our parents who in turn have to carry the burdens of their parents. Perhaps it would be easier not to know."

"Would it really be easier, Paul? We are what we are, because of what we bring with us, surely. I don't mean just biologically — you know more about this than I do — but there is the whole load which was carried before we were born. Carried not only by our parents and grandparents but by the generations before that."

"And then there is our own life, what we have experienced so far, what has impressed itself on us, how we have coped, what we have learnt."

"Even all this is not enough."

"Not enough, Martin? What else? Nature and nurture, both are equally important. What we bring into our lives and what we acquire from the moment of conception: is this not enough to be heaped upon us?"

"And yet, Paul, there is still something else. It is difficult to say what it is. It's a mysterious element in us which makes us unique. When I was very small, I stood in front of a mirror sometimes and I was aware of something inside me: I am I because I am myself. I shuddered and became giddy thinking about it and ran to the bed and hid my head in the cushions. But then I found comfort in the thought that this very kernel within me was being specially cared for by some force outside me."

"And all this was going on in your thinking when you were little?"

"Yes, but I would not have been able to find words to explain it."

"I always knew that you are the more fortunate of us two, Martin."

"But there is also much pain, Paul, believe me."

They had rested by the side of the road. It was a beautiful, quiet evening. The slowly sinking sun seemed to know nothing of the turmoil beneath her. The stillness was almost painful.

Then the brothers lifted their heads. There was a distinct sound. Slight, very slight at first, more like a whisper. But then the rumbling came nearer to them, the noise took form: a speck at the end of a very straight road, a speck which quickly grew into an ever increasing shape together with the swelling roar. The brothers watched the tank stopping fifty yards behind them.

They were shocked to hear German voices:

"It can't be far from here, Albert."

"Let's go on a little further."

The big machine, grinding and crunching as if in anger, passed by.

The road to Warsaw was not free.

The brothers had come too late.

The brothers were too horrified to think.

They bedded themselves down underneath the trees, seeking shelter under Paul's coat.

Our despair cannot be described. Obviously there was no possibility of walking to Warsaw. The tank had come from the direction of the capital. German troops were likely to be stationed all around us. Even if the Germans had not yet occupied Warsaw, it was pointless to walk through their lines. What should we do? Go back to Lukow, find somewhere to hide? But then we were not safe from the Poles. With the Germans we could at least make ourselves understood. We could report to a German officer, stand to attention and shout: "We are the Jews Paul and Martin Rosen." We would be bullied, but then, perhaps, the German soldiers would let us go or make arrangements to send us to a labour camp.

Paul said that he did not want to carry on any longer.

I asked him what he meant. He pulled from his pocket an old match box. Inside was a new razor blade, still wrapped in oily paper.

"Where did you get this from?"

"I bought it on the way, for just such an occasion. Even you, Martin, must realise that there is no point in going on. All the roads are closed to us. We have done all we can. There is a limit to everything, as the saying goes. The limit has been reached."

There was nothing I could say in reply. I had no wish to face this day or any other without him. I could think of nothing to say to help him or me.

All I had thought and pondered over and reflected on had led us to a small, sharp bit of steel.

'Our lives mean nothing after all,' I thought, 'our death will wipe out whatever else was planned for us. If dying was not part of the design, we shall hurt Him, let's pay Him out.'

We went into the undergrowth and crouched in the bushes. Paul started to scratch his wrist. His blood made the shape of some flower on the palm of his hand. He asked me whether I had a handkerchief and I dug out of my pocket a grey rag and wound it round his wrist. Then we got up, wordless, and walked on in the direction of the capital.

"Of course, the German army is not the SA or the SS," said Martin.

"No, I guess not."

"It is possible they will ignore us."

"It's possible."

"After all, they have got more important things to see to."

"Yes."

"There are no concentration camps in Poland. They are not likely to lay on transport to Dachau for the brothers Rosen."

"No, it is not likely."

"We're not important enough."

"We are unimportant. Yes."

"They might even help us."

"Help us? How?"

"There is a note in our passports which says that we are not allowed to re-enter Germany or any country occupied by Germany."

"Well?"

184

"Can't you see? There is no reason for them to hold us? To them it must make more sense to let us go on to Warsaw, where we have a chance to leave the country."

"Perhaps it would be more sensible. But reason doesn't come into it."

"How d'you mean?"

"If people were reasonable, we would not be in the situation we are now. Everything is unreasonable, irrational, insane."

"But don't you see, it would be in their own interest to let us go? We are only a hindrance. Why should they want to bother?"

"Why indeed?"

"It might be to our advantage to meet with the German army."

"You have the gift of seeing beautiful flowers where there are weeds."

"Not all Germans are Jew baiters. Soldiers are not necessarily Party members."

They passed a German cavalry patrol. Horses were being watered and fed. There was the smell of animal hide and leather. The soldiers chatted. Some threw glances at the brothers. The brothers threaded themselves through without being stopped. Only a hundred yards more. Then the road was clear of people.

"Don't look back," said Martin.

Two hours later they saw the ruins of a town in front of them: shells of houses, only the church still stood, apparently unharmed, its tower overlooking the debris. They passed a signpost: to Warsaw — 55 kilometres.

'Perhaps we shall get there tomorrow,' thought Martin, but he was too weary to talk. Paul was feverish. The diarrhoea had weakened him. Next to Martin, he stepped out as if drawn forward in spite of his frailty. Around a bend there was a group of German soldiers and on the meadow, sucked dry by the merciless sun, was a large crowd of men, Polish soldiers and civilians. The brothers were ordered to join the ever growing column.

The journey to Warsaw had come to an end. The journey as prisoners was about to start.

185

Extracts from Paul's diary:

16th September:
We are captured together with hundreds of Polish soldiers and civilians — all of us had tried to get to Warsaw. We march into the town of Garwolin and are locked up inside a church.

17th September:
We remain in the church.
Afternoon: A further march. Imprisoned in another church. What are they going to do with us?

18th September:
March to Siedlce (over 50 kilometres?). We stay the night in an open air camp.

19th September:
We are being divided up into three groups: Soldiers, civilians and Jews. We march from Siedlce to Wegrow. The Jews make up the last group and must run most of the time in order to keep up with the others. The German soldiers see to it, that no one lags behind. My brother is hit by one of the soldiers. I am weeping. I can't control it. They remove our watches. In order to be able to keep up, Martin throws away the little case. The distance between Siedlce and Wegrow is about 30 km. We arrive in Wegrow in the evening and stay in the open air once more. It is raining.

There is little I can add to Paul's sparse sentences. We were both in a state of shock. This may account for the fact that I can remember so very little about the march to Wegrow.

Churches or fields were the only places big enough to hold us. We desecrated the churches, urinating and defecating in the side chapels. Food rations consisted of biscuits as hard as stones and a little soup. Once a priest poured some milk from a small jug into mugs. Like an old painting, hands stretched out, begging, the priest in his cassock holding the jug away from the crowd so that no milk should get spilt. Paul and I leaning somewhere in the aisle against a pillar. We hummed

186

Mozart's *Laudate Dominum*. It felt more secure in a church than on a field. There was still the scent of incense trapped within the solid walls. On the fields one did not feel protected. Soldiers were stationed around them to prevent our escape. We never thought of escaping. Paul was very ill during the long march from Garwolin to Wegrow. He had to fall behind because of his diarrhoea. A soldier was posted to wait for him and then he hurried him along to join the large column again. From time to time he leaned on me, indeed he was very weak. He wrote that he was weeping. I cannot remember this. But I do remember the soldier hitting me. He probably objected to my looking at him, he was walking a few metres away from me. 'Such an ordinary man,' I thought, 'who was doing ordinary things at home with his wife and his children.' And I wondered whether there was some despair even in his eyes. He did not like being scrutinised in this way. He came over to me, shouted and hit me. He was one of the soldiers in charge of the rear part of the column consisting of Jews who had been separated and had all the running to do to keep up with the rest. The soldier abused them. He threatened them. He used the butt of his rifle. He was hateful, but there was nothing in his face I could hate. Paul and I did not look like these Jews. We were beardless and were not dressed like them. We could easily have passed for Poles. It would have made the marching easier. But the thought of joining the Poles never entered our minds. We were Jews. We belonged to the Jewish group.

It was raining during the night on the field in Wegrow. Paul was so ill that we had no choice. He had to report to the camp commander the following morning. He was informed that he would be taken to the nearby military hospital. He requested that I should be permitted to go with him. This was refused. I saw him: a frail, fleeting figure in his light, checked coat which had become part of us both, standing up but slightly bent in the army lorry, looking around him, hoping to spot me. I waved but the lorry left the field without Paul seeing me. I was alone.

Loss and relief. Emptiness. Living without purpose. Now I

could really not care what was going to happen to me. There was neither sorrow nor mourning. I knew I had lost him. But somebody would care for him. He would be looked after in hospital. They would give him meals. He would be treated as a patient. Perhaps we shall meet, some day, somewhere. But he will be well then. He will be able to carry his own burden. How I loved him. What pain he gave me. His suffering. His despair. Now there was nothing that mattered. Nothing. I walked around the field, amidst these hundreds of people.

'Nothing matters,' I thought, 'I do not have to pretend any more. All is beyond my understanding. I do not have to pretend that I understand. His head will rest on a soft white pillow and instead of the old coat he will be covered with a blanket. He matters. I don't. He is more important than I. His anguish was also mine. Now, alone, there is nothing. No fear, no torment, no agony. What a relief. There is nothing to feel. There are the men huddling together over small fires cooking roots and potatoes. Sentries surround the camp. Prisoners and soldiers are far away. There is nothing in front, reaching out, wanting me. Nobody demands anything from me. I don't have anything to give. I am sure they will look after him properly. They won't ill-treat him. They won't dare. He is sick, you know, he is sick. He needs care. I don't need it. He does. My brother does. You must understand, he is most important to me. How is he? How I miss him. But he will be saved. Saved from himself. Saved from me. I failed him. I should not have let him go. I am free now. Free from him. I can sit down without him. I can look at the stubble of grass. Still damp from last night's rain. I can look up. Fast clouds chasing each other. Look over there, legs move without bodies. And there, the whining of a praying Jew.

'And there, busy young men, busy young men emptying their rucksacks, camp gear, food. And one amongst them who is smiling. He does not know that I am watching him. He is smiling. The others look at him and smile at him and serve him. They give him things. A shirt or a mug, or a plate, like presents. Then there is a sharing out. How many are there? Four, five I think, yes, five. They are dressed like young people on a field trip. I remember Toni. We called him dwarf.

188

He was a small boy. Dwarf could have been one of the five. He prided himself on always being prepared. He would find food. Cook it. The stars would tell him where he was. Life was an adventure for him. Emergencies were a challenge. A challenge he could meet. He would survive, always survive and come out of the experience, more skilled, more determined, richer. But he is not here, he does not belong to this little group. How I had admired him. He could mould the events, events did not take him over. Unlike me, who is always the slave of events. Gagged. Twisted. Chained. Look at them over there. Close to each other without touching. Every move, every gesture, every step has its purpose. And that young man in the middle. Is he a teacher? Their teacher? There is a glow around him, an invisible glow which, like a strong beam, falls on me. I look away. I can't bear it.'

"Do you want anything to eat?"

A member of the group had come over to Martin and was bending over him.

"If you have anything to spare," Martin stuttered.

"Come along."

They had prepared some soup and there were hot potatoes in crisp skins. Martin did not sit with them. He sat a little apart and while he ate, he wondered.

'They do not fit in here. Who are they? What are they doing here? Students, perhaps. Polish students who were on their way to the University of Warsaw? Caught but not caught. Not caught because they had been caught well prepared. They are unlike all the other prisoners camping on the field. That strange quiet leader, who is he? How I should like to serve him too. If only I could be one of them. If only I could be his disciple too.'

Martin was called to meet him.

"Are you on your own?"

"My brother has been taken to the military hospital.'

The slight nod of the head signalled a gentle dismissal.

It grew dark. Martin settled down near the others. He felt safe. He dreamt of Paul.

Paul was back next day. Martin embraced him. Paul explained:

"The military hospital did not want to admit me. They told me to go to the Jewish hospital. But that hospital was full. I spent the night in the synagogue. And suddenly I realised I had left you. There was only one thought in my mind. I must come back here. For once, for the first time, I knew what to do. To come back. Now I don't mind so much being ill. I am not afraid of the future any more. We are together. That is all I wanted when I was trying to find sleep in the synagogue. This morning, walking out of the synagogue, I saw a German soldier washing himself under a pump. I went to him and asked where the Polish prisoners had their camp. He looked up at me. You should have seen his face, Martin. I think he thought I was mad. 'What do you want to go there for?' he said. I told him my brother was in there and that I wanted to join him. He showed me the way. I asked one of the soldiers outside the camp to let me in. He stared at me and then he thrashed me with his rifle butt and pushed me inside. I can't blame him. For someone to come and ask to be taken prisoner is too much. We all fear becoming insane."

Later the brothers discussed the future. Somehow they had both changed. They seemed to be ready to face whatever there was to face. The short separation had aged them. They knew there was the distinct possibility that they would be taken to a labour camp somewhere in Germany or perhaps even to a concentration camp. It was likely they would be split up, eventually. But whatever happened, it must be their aim to survive this war, if not for their own sakes for the sake of the parents. They knew now that there was a stronger bond between the four of them than they had cared to admit. There was great love within the family. Such ties should not be broken. They would all meet again after the war and would then be ready to build up relationships between each other which were sounder, firmer than before. The parents were probably suffering more at this very moment, than they did. They had probably become very close to one another in their experience of sharing the anxiety for their sons.

"We shall see them again," said Paul.

They crept under Paul's coat, at peace.

'He came back,' thought Martin, 'he could have saved himself, but he came back because of me. The parents are waiting. We shall arrive, one day we shall be with them. Pull us towards you, step by step, a little every day. Wait for us. We shall arrive.'

Next day the leader of the little group came to them. Another young man was with him, holding two mugs of hot tea. He handed them to the brothers.

"Your brother?" asked the leader and Martin nodded.

"How are you feeling?"

"I am ill. But there was no bed free in the hospital. So I returned."

Martin had already told Paul about these mysterious young people who had affected him so deeply with their ability to cope, their dignity and above all their concern. Now Paul felt the strange power which seemed to radiate from this man.

"Will you be able to manage?" asked the leader.

"I am not going to leave my brother," Paul replied.

Then the two left. Paul said:

"Who are they, I wonder?"

"They are what we think they are," Martin said.

"You are speaking in riddles again."

"No. You already said it. They are people to be wondered at."

Some time later the leader returned — was he the leader because he was loved by the others? — together with a stranger who wore a yellow armband. They both looked at Paul who was in pain and then into Martin's face. The man with the armband ordered Martin to open his mouth. Martin felt humiliated. His ugly upper lip did not concern anyone else. And his teeth neglected for weeks had become green.

'I smell,' he thought, 'and the scars have become inflamed. I am a repulsive cripple who is exposing himself. Now I am utterly naked, raw, all my wounds are revealed.'

Tears ran down Martin's cheeks.

"Come," the man with the armband said.

"You will both see the doctor," the leader added and he smiled.

Paul and Martin left the camp, the man with the armband at their side. He was an auxiliary Polish policeman recruited by the Germans. They passed the armed German soldiers guarding the field. They did not take any notice of them. It was only a short distance to the little town of Wegrow. They came to a low wooden building. The policeman stopped and let the brothers enter. He did not follow them. The place was quite empty but for a bench. The brothers waited for someone to come. They waited for a long time. But no one came.

They looked at each other and shrugged their shoulders.

Then Paul said: "How much longer should we wait." It was not a question. Martin got up.

"I'll just look outside." He came back at once.

"There is no one outside. The policeman has left. We'd better go."

They left. There were some people in the street but the brothers were ignored.

"Perhaps we should go to the Jewish Hospital," said Paul, "they may have a vacant bed today. I know where it is. In the market place."

"You know we are free, Paul, they freed us."

"Yes. Who can explain this?"

"So much cannot be explained, Paul, getting on the train, the destruction of the police station in Lublin, the returned papers and now our escape from the camp."

"It is your faith, Martin. Your faith is carrying us."

"No, no, Paul. My faith is weak. Often I think that I have lost it altogether. Your despair is also my despair and I am often filled with fear, with such fear."

"And yet . . ."

They had arrived at the Jewish Hospital. This time they were prepared to admit Paul. But there was no bed for Martin.

"I don't mind," said Martin to one of the nurses, "I shall find somewhere to sleep. A corner in the corridor, perhaps, if you don't mind."

Extract from 'Travel Guide: Poland' (1970)* :

'Wegrow — population 9000, filling station, district town on the right bank of the Liwiec. Tanning industry. Artistic Folk-handicraft centre. Weaving Mill. Borough charter granted in 1441. From the mid 16th cent. the grain trade with Gdansk developed. One of the most important centres of the reformation in Poland. The Arian synod established in 1570 a seminary, printing house, school and hospital. Meeting place of various protestant synods (1565-1788). The town was destroyed in the last war (1939-45).

In the market place stands a 16th cent. parish church*, rebuilt in 1703-06 in Gothic-baroque . . . in the sacristy a 'magician's mirror' which according to legend belonged to the 16th century magician Twardowski (a Polish Faust). At No 26 Market Place the Gdansk House* a former inn in early 18th cent. Baroque. East of the Parish Church a baroque church and former Franciscan monastery 1693-1706. On the Protestant cemetery stands a wooden chapel, 1679. Inside the chapel and in the cemetery there are 17th and 18th century tombstones of Scottish families who settled here in the mid 16th cent.

(Note) Asterisks (*) denote places of special tourist interest.

We knew nothing of the historic beauties of the town, of course. For a week we stayed at the Jewish Hospital. Paul was confined to bed and I hardly ever left the building. Wegrow was occupied by the Germans and I could not take the risk of walking about in the town. Sometimes in the morning, I sneaked out into the street to get some oatmeal or potatoes or apples from a little shop nearby. There was little to eat in the hospital, even for the patients, and I was not entitled to any food. On the floor above the ward was a sort of kitchenette with a gas stove and a few pans. There I cooked some porridge for Paul and myself or I mashed up potatoes with whatever else I could get hold of.

The windows from the ward looked out into the market place. Opposite was the town hall, at least we thought it was the town hall. It could have been the Gdansk House which is referred to in the guide, requisitioned by the authorities for official business. Anyhow, the building was important. I kept an eye on it. On its roof the swastika.

*Published by Sport 1 Turystyka, Warszawa, Poland.

193

j

In front of it armoured vehicles, horses and parading German soldiers. Sounds of shouted commands and clicked heels.

In the hospital one felt safe. The Germans did not take any interest in what was going on here. Patients were mostly wounded Polish soldiers.

We did not know what the military position was. We did not know that Warsaw would surrender a few days after our arrival here. We did not know that most of Poland had been taken by the Germans and that the Russians had invaded the eastern part of Poland and were on their way to Wegrow.

Only one thought was in my mind: that we should stay here as long as possible, until Paul had recovered. I did not think further ahead. There was no future.

I am trying to recall how I spent the long hours during this week. But my mind is hazy. Did I assist in any way in the hospital? Did I clean up the wards? Did I help the attendants? Fetch and carry for them? I don't know. Did I go round the ward and talk to the patients? No, I could not speak Polish. But there were mornings, afternoons and evenings. How did I occupy myself? I remember looking out into the market place for long periods, but, surely, I could not have sat by the window for hours on end observing what the Germans were doing. There are many gaps in my narration which I cannot fill.

The week was a pause, an interval, a reprieve for Paul and me. Exhausted and at breaking point, we could live for a short time now in a kind of no-man's-land, where one need not make any decisions and where no demands were made. There was only the constant problem of how to still one's hunger. Perhaps in such a situation one does not have a sense of time and there is therefore no reason to fill it. It is difficult, perhaps impossible, for me to see myself living in such a limbo, now that I am so removed from it. I am looking at myself from here, from a distance, as if I had been someone else, an alien living in some bizarre land, where everything was fantastic. I have to remind myself that I was not just a witness, an observer, but that I took part, lived through it, thought and suffered. It is always difficult to imagine that one can bear what others seem able to bear. But we can bear more than we think we can.

194

Inside you something is being transformed. Mercifully. An act of grace. A signal of love. But you cannot hold onto it altogether. Some memories remain. Others are lost, handed back. Perhaps, I comfort myself, suffering is too precious an experience to hold onto. I cannot remember it completely any more. Perhaps what I have forgotten is too important to remember. Perhaps the time spent in the Wegrow Hospital was a time to take stock, to find myself again.

I had no knowledge that there was a 'magician's mirror' in the church which must have been nearby. If I had known, I would have dared to go there without telling Paul, hoping to see in it, if only for a fraction of a moment, where we would be in six months. Still alive? In Poland? Many times I had prayed for just such a flash, a quick revelation. But there was no magician's mirror in the hospital. The great magician kept his intentions to himself.

*   *   *   *

I did not get to know Wegrow.

But I did not really know my home town, Breslau, either. Many years after the war, when I went back to Germany for the first time, I bought a town plan of Breslau as it was when I was a child.

Breslau had been defended block by block, street by street, house by house, when the Russian army entered it from the south during the last stages of the war.

But the map shows no scars. The same one, enlarged, had hung at the front of the classroom of my Junior School.

The parks, cemeteries and open spaces are coloured in different shades of green. Hospitals, stations and the university are shown in red. Residential areas are beige and the river Oder, which flows through the city, and its branches, are bright blue. A map attractive to a child. I am looking at a plan of a city which does not exist any more.

This is where I lived as a child: here are the familiar streets and squares and green spots. What I remember is not yet dead. But how little I knew of Breslau. The first sixteen years of my life I spent in Breslau. But only got to

195

know parts of it.

We lived in a suburb in the south. It is the south which I mainly remember. It is the south which was in utter ruins at the end of the war. What was left had to be demolished. I wonder what has been built where our house stood? Perhaps there is now only an empty space.

Other parts of the city did not belong to me: they had to be reached by tram, generally. There was the daily journey to Grammar School, no joy for me, and then the trips on special occasions. When I was older I cycled, but I avoided going into the town. I did not care for the bustle of the traffic. I preferred to get out of the city, further south where I could stand still, close my eyes and feel the wind.

My vision is limited. Most of my memories of when I was small are confined to the left quarter of the map. The street where our house stood (it was our house, although we lived only in a flat on the second floor) was S-shaped. It ran into one of the main roads which led to the centre, the Ring — the old market place — with its famous gothic town hall. I only went there occasionally, for instance, when I was allowed to accompany mother on one of her shopping trips, or when we went to see father in his shop which was in the old part not far from the Ring. My anchorage was of course at home or within the vicinity of our house.

There was the goods train a few hundred metres away. The South Park in all its seasonal splendour. The little pond at the other end of the street in the middle of an unassuming recreation area — on which no child was allowed to play, walking on grass was an offence, but you could occupy yourself quietly sitting on the bench — and the tiny hill beyond the railway bridge, which was called the 'Children's Zobten', alluding to the big mountain where the Lindens had their weekend home. There we tried to fly kites and went tobogganing in winter.

As I did not do much work for school, I spent a lot of time playing in the streets, which in those days were practically traffic-free.

But I felt safe only in the bug-ridden flat and in the over-heated room which I shared, when I was little, with the maid. The space at the back of the house was damp-smelling but in front there were a number of lilac trees and it was grandfather who cut off the twigs when they were in bloom, brought them into the flat which was for once filled with a sweet aroma. We had many plants in the front rooms and the winter-garden, with exotic multi-coloured leaves. Sometimes they flowered, often unexpectedly — an explosion of dyed crowns — always miraculously. I touched them with care. I did not want to hurt them. My mother looked after them with great skill and devotion. The pots were examined, the plants spoken to (mother had given some of them boys' or girls' names), watered and pruned and re-potted in the winter-garden, where mother did most of her indoor gardening. The winter-garden, whose glass front stuck out into the open, high above the street, was my Africa. Here I could pretend better than anywhere else in the flat. It could be the cabin of a flying aeroplane skimming the sea, or it could be the lift in one of the stores I sometimes went to with mother, with its double doors which I clanged shut like the lift-boy I had seen. But often it was some foreign land with strange trees and animals and terrors which I could easily control. I was fearless here. In summer it was so hot in the winter-garden that, lying back in the deckchairs, with glasses of raspberry squash on the little table, even the adults must have sometimes imagined themselves in the tropics.

The glass doors of the winter-garden led to the music room, the best room in the flat. It was almost elegant, with the Bechstein Baby Grand covered with a green silken embroidered fabric with its long tassels, hanging low, golden hair which I touched only when nobody saw me. When Paul or mother played, I often lay underneath the shiny black animal. Then I gently pulled the tassels in time to the music. I rang bells. The furniture here was beautiful. A small, highly polished table, with delicate chairs to match, a kind of tallboy, always locked, displaying china ornaments which my mother particularly liked, also a large silken floor cushion in pastel-green on which rested, eternally, Bully, the soft toy dog whose dark glass eyes stared without remorse at anyone who sat at the keyboard. Prints of well-known actors and dancers hung on the green-gold walls. A fine room, much admired by our visitors.

The lounge — or the gentleman's room as it was ostentatiously called — always smelled of my father's and my grandfather's cigars. It was very large with fitted bookcases, as high as a man, along the whole length of one wall. They held the works of most of the German classics and a great mix of other literature, anything from oriental folk tales (with explicit pictures not meant for my eyes) to *The Death of Queen Victoria*. The family was very proud of this mass of books. Of course, I was not allowed to dance on the heavy carpet, but I loved to twirl round and round until giddiness overcame me and I had to stagger to one of the leathered armchairs and fall into it, relieved but excited. Upholstered fitted seats were meant for the guests: chatting to each other in the alcove gave a feeling of intimacy. In a little niche above stood a small fragile lamp which was lit on some days in memory of members of the family who had died. (I wondered whether the dead had come during the night and had switched on the light themselves.) On a special plant-table by the window grew aggressive, spiky cacti which I disliked. I was tempted once to cut off the nasty needles with scissors but I feared what my mother would do to me, if I did.

We only used the dining-room on Sundays and on special occasions. Otherwise it was reserved for the guests. The dining-room with its traditional heavy furniture and parquet floor, smelled of floor wax furniture polish and the fluid with which my mother cleaned the silver. (No servant was allowed to touch the precious forks, knives and spoons. This was the task of the Mistress.)

This was the world of the adults. Paul and I were not encouraged to go into any of these rooms, unless there was a particular reason to do so, we certainly were not allowed to play there. Paul, of course, spent a lot of time in the music room and often I sneaked in as well, not so much because I wanted to listen to him playing, but I wanted to be part of this world, so full of promise of the good things to come when I was grown up. 'Father must be rich,' I thought, 'I too shall be rich one day.' Indeed, one could sink into the armchairs and the thick carpets were soft. Paul practised Mozart, mother's scent hung in the air and the afternoon sun stole through the venetian blinds and painted the walls with red-gold streamers.

But the back rooms provided a contrast. True, the parents' bedroom was luxurious, all in white matt varnish and with an enormous blue-veined marble wash-stand and running water. We rarely came in here, apart from saying good-bye to mother when we left for school in the mornings. Where Paul and I reigned it looked rather different.

There was Paul's room where grandfather also slept, behind a screen. Here were some curious pieces of furniture which grandfather had brought with him when he moved to us, in a style unnecessarily ornate, a jumble of odd tables, chairs, wardrobes, chest of drawers, also in my room, next to Paul's, an unattractive assembly of odd bits and pieces. But what an arena for play!

The door between my room and Paul's was hardly ever closed, unless one of us suffered from some kind of infection, or Paul wanted to be left in peace. A swing had been fitted between the two rooms. I could fly into the distance where nobody could find me and dream.

I had a desk to do my homework on. It had a slanting lid which could be raised like the desks at school, to store books and paper underneath. My feet rested on a wooden grill. By turning the desk upside down or laying it on its side, I could use it for different imaginative games: some craft going into the sky, a ship, a car. (I had not forgotten my days in the kindergarten.) The wooden grill was also very useful. I hung bottles and tins and pieces of wood on it it. It made the ideal percussion instrument. Paul improved on it and put it to better use. He accompanied himself, listening to the radio through the headphones. This was not much fun for me.

There was also the large heavy table which stood in the middle of my room. We must have had it since we were babies. With some effort the top could be lifted off and one looked inside a zinc bath tub where Nanny had washed us. It still smelt of something disagreeable. Perhaps Nanny had used some particular obnoxious brand of soap or disinfectant. But we made some use of the tub. One could hide things inside. The grown-ups would never find them.

I did not like the cream-coloured chest of drawers with the mirror behind it. The maid used it when she slept in my room. I avoided looking at myself in the mirror. I did not like my face.

Between my room and the kitchen, was the cook's bed-chamber, hardly more than a cubicle. How anyone could have put up with such living conditions, I don't know. But our servants stayed with us, generally for long periods. Lotte was always given violet perfume for Christmas. There was always the scent of violets in her little room.

But there was another smell in the back rooms. The smell of 'Flit' which we sprayed diligently on the walls to kill the bedbugs. They lived in the walls ("for seven years" one of the maids told us), and crawled down to our beds at night and settled on our arms and legs. They bit and sucked. They loved warm children's limbs. A squashed bug stank. 'An odour of death,' I thought. But most times the bugs had disappeared in the mornings as if they knew that we hated them. They had left behind itchy weals on the skin and little spots of blood on the sheets.

My poor mother, so meticulous about the appearance of our home, demanding from the servants a rigid regime of sweeping, brushing, wiping and scrubbing, my mother who supervised the airing and beating of bedclothes, who saw to it that the furniture — particularly the furniture in the front rooms — was dusted and polished, the floor waxed, the linoleum washed, my mother was convinced that the infestation of bugs was another proof that life had heaped misfortunes upon her. She was blameless.

The kitchen was not only the domain of the cook and the maid (later there was only a servant who did both cooking and cleaning), it also belonged to me. I felt warm in it. The servants made only one demand on me: to love them. I

200

loved them.

The kitchen led to the passage which connected the humble part of the flat with the one reserved for the grown-ups of the family and their guests. We passed two lavatories. The first one was used by the servants, the other, close to the entrance hall, was for us. It was also the bathroom. I hardly ever entered the servants' lavatory, I used it only in an emergency. It consisted of a wooden board, well scrubbed, with a hole in the middle. I remember asking my mother once why the servants could not use our lavatory, which was so much more comfortable. I was told that the servants preferred to have their own lavatory. I was not convinced. Perhaps, I thought, I was too young to understand why the servants should prefer to wipe themselves with squares of cut up newspaper rather than our soft toilet paper. I did not want to ask the cook.

When I was fourteen we had to move to another flat. My father had recently taken over a chain of shoe shops. They were not a success. For the past year the Nazis had been in power. Father was getting worried about meeting his financial obligations. Household expenses had to be cut down. We had to move into a smaller flat, in a less desirable district. The rent was cheap and it was the landlord who was responsible for the upkeep. The proceeds of the sale of the house paid for the debts father had incurred. We had come down in the world.

I shall never forget the move. While I regretted leaving the house where I had spent my childhood, I was excited by the prospect of living somewhere else. Some of the furniture had to be sold, there was no room in the new flat for all of it and Frau Seeliger had specially come from across the border, and had a field day. She had never shown an interest in furniture before. She paid a little for a lot. The removal van had swallowed up, like some hungry beast, all our possessions. Some of these stood for some time on the pavement, naked and unclaimed, while small giggling children were watching, and I too stood and watched, strangely embarrassed. My father had given instructions to the removal men but he soon left and mother spent the day with friends. Her anxiety about possible breakages would have caused annoyance.

It was difficult enough for her to see the packer wrapping up the glasses, the china, the vases and all the other fragile objects. Repeatedly she had warned him to be very careful, extra cautious, particularly gentle with this, that or the other. Finally the man had lost his temper:

"If Madam wishes to do her own packing, I shall be happy to leave."

But it was mother who left the dining-room where he was busy stacking away, into a huge tea chest, our best cups and saucers.

I told him, "You musn't mind what she says. She is always like this." I flushed. I knew I had been disloyal. I knew that I did wrong in talking like this.

'I shall be punished for this,' I thought, 'I can never get away with it like other people. Something unpleasant is bound to happen to me.'

I did not know that punishment was going to be meted out that same evening.

The van had been unloaded. Furniture and cases had been dispersed in the various rooms of the new flat. There still seemed to be too much stuff. I was to sleep in the parents' bedroom for the night. The place was in chaos. The handyman from my father's shop was expected to set things aright the following morning. I went to bed before mother arrived. I told father that the day had tired me out, and that I had to get up early for school.

The quarrel started as soon as mother entered the hall. The quarrel became a collision of two people who had given up pretending to respect each other. A flood of ugly words. Recall of past incidents which should have been forgotten. Insinuations and accusations. Open charges. Blaming and counterblaming. Screamed exclamations. Resentments. Wounds. Old scars broken open.

The carpenters had come the previous day to adapt the row of bookcases which had been dismantled in our old flat. They had to be refitted in our new lounge which had an awkward shape and was, in any case, smaller. Clearly, the carpenters had made a mess of it. There were gaps between the units, and there was one case which stood on its own on the opposite wall. The glass was broken. There were visible scratches and one or two shelves had been damaged.

My mother blamed father for the rotten work of the craftsmen.

"You can't even see to it that work in our home is done properly."

"What did you want me to do? Oversee them while they are working?"

"You have always been unreliable. This is another example."

"What do you mean?"

"You have asked workers to do the job who know nothing about it."

"The firm was recommended to me."

"The firm is probably a little cheaper than reputable craftsmen."

"This is rubbish. If you would have spent some time here yesterday, instead of gossiping with your so-called friends over coffee, all would have been well."

"So I am to blame. Of course, it is I who am responsible. The next thing you will say is that I am responsible for your business disasters."

"If you had taken a little more interest in my business, perhaps it would have helped."

"You mean standing behind the till like the wives of your delightful brothers."

"I mean a little less culture and a little more concern for mundane matters."

"But you are not interested in business. You are only interested in a fine pair of legs. You're running after every shop girl who makes eyes at you."

"I'm a normal man. We have not lived like man and wife for years."

"That is no reason for being unfaithful."

"Oh, leave me alone, woman. Let me go my way."

"Your way? And what about those bills which are never paid? And the bailiff who came and stuck labels under the grand piano and the good furniture? That's not your responsibility either, is it?"

"You know as well as I do that all the bills had been paid. I can't help it if there was a muddle in the office there. I didn't get a receipt."

"You are lying to me."

"You'd better watch our what you are saying, the boy is here."

"Martin has to learn about his father, as Paul did."

"You set Paul against me. I am glad the boy is away in Prague now."

"You are too busy with your women to take an interest in your sons. You don't really love them as much as you say you do."

And then father cried, a small, pitiful almost soundless sobbing. I heard mother calming him.

"I should not have said that. I do know that you love them. But the pitcher goes so often to the well that finally it breaks."

While the arguing was going on, I shivered under the blankets. 'Oh God, if they would only stop.'

I did not want to hear, but I had to listen. I knew my parents fought. But this was worse than ever. Why don't I jump out of bed and scream at them? I loved them. How could they do this to each other? How could they do this to me? I hated them. I hated myself for hating them. Don't they know that I am listening to what they are saying? Why don't I shout at them 'stop it you two, stop it'. Don't you know you are murdering me? Why do I feel so paralysed, powerless, feeble, weak, so weak?

And then I remembered what I had said to the packer about my mother and I realised that I was being punished now.

All was still. I listened to the quiet breathing of the parents. Father had stopped crying and there was mother's familiar little cough.

There were other occasions when I was woken in the middle of the night by the harsh voices of my arguing parents. One night father called Paul and they both ran to the bathroom where mother had locked herself in. She was screaming that she was going to swallow all the aspirin tablets in the medicine cupboard. Paul wept in despair and after a long time mother opened the door and they fell on each other's necks.

Often there was a row when father, who had promised to join mother at a party, did not do so. He did not like these social occasions and could not comprehend why mother so enjoyed the company of people who had nothing better to do than to brag about their successes in life.

*   *   *   *

Paul was getting better. There was a hint of confidence in his eyes. I sat on his bed.

"You remember how we celebrated the parents' twenty-fifth wedding anniversary in Kattowitz, Martin?"

"I did not feel at ease on that occasion."

"Not at ease? Why?"

"Was there really something to celebrate? Celebrating the fact that they had stuck it out together for twenty-five years?"

"But they achieved something, Martin. They did not run away from each other or from us."

"It's a sad marriage, Paul."

"Sad perhaps. But necessary."

"Necessary? Why?"

"How would you have managed, Martin, when you were small, if the parents had separated?"

"I don't think I could have managed, Paul. Of course I did not realise the difficulties in their marriage. Perhaps I did not want to know. I needed to believe that everything was secure around me. As far as I was concerned, we all loved one another."

"There you are. You see how important it was for them to remain together."

"They had to pay a big price. Neither of them is happy."

"What is happiness, Martin? In their circle of relatives and friends divorce was unthinkable."

"But it is true, isn't it, that Prof Fried, you know the surgeon who operated on me, wanted to marry mother?"

"So she says. And it may well be true. But I don't think she would have married him anyhow. It would have been

205

an admission of failure. Mother can never admit failure."

"And father?"

"Father really adores her, you know. He always refers to her as the pure undefiled mother of his children. He knew from the outset that he had married a woman superior to him, and he probably still sees mother as the highly cultured, sensitive, vulnerable plant which only he can look after. In spite of her anger about his lack of achievements."

"But mother does not love him."

"Oh Martin. Love means so many different things."

"But without it, Paul, how can two people live together for the whole of their lives?"

"They need each other."

"Need each other?"

"Father needs mother because she is what he never can be — cultured, perceptive, intuitive, a lover of books, theatre, music and then she is the mother of his children."

"And mother? Why does she need him?"

"It could be that she sees her own failing in him, her husband. She can blame him for what she herself has not achieved. After all, she was not strong enough to resist her parents. She did not become a singer. She did not marry the man she had loved."

"What a pair. But we can't help talking about them."

"Well, they are the most important people in our lives."

"I hardly ever saw mother being so jolly as on the evening with the Zimmermanns when we congratulated the parents and drank wine."

"She was perhaps too jolly, don't you think?"

"Yes there was something forced about the whole evening."

"Perhaps mother knew intuitively that we would be separated from her. She drank a lot, I remember. In the end father had to take her glass away. She talked and talked about the past, as if it had consisted only of joyful events, and then she painted a rosy picture of the future in England for us all."

"Do you think she believed in it?"

"No, I don't think so. It was her way of saying 'good-bye'."

"And a week later the parents left."

"And we stayed behind and had to learn how much they meant to us."

"Yes, Paul."

"You still believe we shall be reunited?"

"Paul, I am afraid that my prayers sometimes are prayers for survival rather than prayers for reaching the parents. Perhaps I am pretending to you and to myself that what matters most is to be with them. Perhaps I just want to live."

"Well, living comes first."

"But then, suddenly, when I expect it least, I feel their pull and then I am convinced we shall be with them. We are part of them. Yes, Paul, we shall be with them, one day.

One day, looking into the market place through the window, I saw some Jews sweeping the place. Laughing German soldiers stood around and pointed their fingers at them. The bearded, oddly-dressed men caused amusement. I remembered Paul's lesson in how to use the broom in the transit camp. How I had suffered for him. But watching now the degradation of a small group of people to which I belonged I was glad that neither Paul nor I were amongst them. Had I become hard, unfeeling? Should I not go out and join them? But I did not, and I watched the scene with ugly fascination. What had happened to me? And what had happened to these young soldiers? They had not always behaved like this, I was certain. Can we change so much in such a short time?

If I had power over others, how would I use it? No, I would not wish to cause pain or shame my captives. I am certain of it. But would I have enough pluck to withdraw, to say: no, comrades I am not going to take part in this disgusting game. Leave me out. I know I would not be able to stop them in whatever they felt like doing, but what about making a gesture? Would I make it? Tell them that they are degrading themselves in the act of degrading others? Or would I, half-heartedly perhaps, or with just a little sensation of self-importance, participate? After all, no real harm is done. The streets are filthy, they have to be swept, it's in their interest and in ours. And then, our prisoners have to learn who the new masters are. Could I risk being called a spoil-sport, the outsider, a lover of the enemy? But if the situation were reversed, what then? If there was an opportunity to treat the German soldiers, these brutish louts, as they treated the Jews, if, I say, I could take revenge on these dogs who have broken up our family and made us suffer, if I could make them suffer, would I refuse? Or would I run out, laughing, and make them, not just sweep the place but eat the dirt, make them eat it, make them, make them.

In the afternoon they carried in an old rabbi who had been stabbed by a soldier. He seemed to be in bad shape. He was undressed and laid on the bed, which was opposite Paul's. There was blood running from his hip. The Rabbi wanted to let us know how seriously he was injured. For hours he was lamenting, groaning, wailing. "Oy, oy, oy, Gottenyu, oy."

Men sat around the bed and prayed. A never ending singsong. I was angry. 'No pain,' I thought, 'can be so bad that one must shout. And how can the others, praying around him, proclaiming God's glory, be of help to him?'

Then another thought occurred to me: 'Perhaps the rabbi feels the pain of his people. Perhaps he was not just howling for himself, perhaps he was lamenting for us all, not only for us Jews but for all of us, the degraders and the degraded. And the men standing there with nodding heads, assent, rhythmically and precisely, that there *is* a God, in spite of the ghastliness, in spite of our muzzled, suppressed race, in spite of our suffering rabbi.'

I had slept on the floor in the corridor for a few nights. Sometimes I walked around the building. The patients were on the ground floor, some people were living on the floor above. The little kitchen which I used, belonged to a withered old woman who was very deaf. There was a door at the end of Paul's ward and having nothing else to do, I dared to open it one afternoon, wondering where it would lead. There were some steps going down into the basement.

208

Here was silence. Groaning and sighing could not be heard here, nor the crisp commands on the market place. To be so alone, all of a sudden, was threatening. I wanted to retreat, to return to what was familiar, back to the window next to Paul's bed or to what I had called 'my corner', where my bedraggled jacket became my pillow and Paul's coat my blanket at night. Why was I not sitting on Paul's bed now, talking to him, giving him some hope? I liked this little hospital and secretly hoped Paul would be unfit to leave for some time. But now I had wandered away, like a toddler, wandered into uncertainty. Some light came from another door, half open. I hesitated but took a few more steps. And stepped into a room. Not just empty space, but a real room. With furniture. There was a cupboard, the drawers pulled out, still with a few pieces of woman's clothing. The wardrobe was sloping to one side, as if slightly drunk, there were a couple of chairs, both broken, their wooden legs intertwined. And a bed. A large bed. Without sheets, but with a blanket and pillows. The small window was broken, fragments of glass covered the floor underneath it. Why had the woman who had lived here departed in such haste: Had she run away from the Germans? But where could she flee to? And why had the window been broken? And why was the room in such a state? Could I perhaps sleep here? It was only a few steps away from Paul. Oh, to sleep in a proper bed, the first time for weeks, did it matter if I slept in somebody's bed? But nobody lived here now. I could not be accused of breaking in.

I rushed back to Paul to ask him. He was my big brother, after all, he would advise me. Paul could not think of a reason why I should not sleep in the room which I had found. I went back later like a child who had found some secret place to hide and lay on the bed. I became giddy. I closed my eyes and was aware of the softness of the mattress, the smoothness of the pillow, the quietness around me. It was almost too much to bear. To lie here, just to lie here for ever. No, not for ever, but there were many hours until morning. I took off my things. I threw my trousers on the floor and hung my jacket on the bedpost. Humming I crept under the blanket and covered my head with it as

Paul and I had done on so many occasions, to enclose ourselves. It was strange to feel my naked, estranged legs, as if they belonged to someone else I had known at some other time, long ago.

I woke up during the night and pulled the blanket away from my eyes. The darkness around me was absolute. Total night. There was a small rustling sound. A mouse? A rat? I cried out and jumped out of bed.

A woman's voice. She spoke Polish first, then Yiddish. I answered in German. I exclaimed that I thought nobody lived here, my brother was a patient upstairs, I had found the room and thought it was unoccupied.

"I shall go back now," I said, "there is a corner in the corridor where I can sleep."

"Hush, still, quite still," said the woman, "you stay here. There is enough room for the two of us."

"I did not break in, I am going now."

"Come back, boy, come."

I went back and soon she came near me and I smelt the strange bitter-sweet odour, a little like the smell of my mother when in the mornings before leaving for school I had gone to her bed and she, still half asleep, had kissed my forehead to make sure I had no fever. I felt the shape of the woman and gently traced with my fingers the outline of the warm form next to me and then I leaned my head against her breasts. And I cried. I cried.

"Why you cry, boy? Hush. Hush."

But I could not stop the weeping. I wept for what had happened in the last month. For Paul. For the parents. The isolation. Agonising moments. The uncertainty. The rabbi. The Jews. Loneliness. Loss. I cried because she was here. Because she held me. Comforted me. Whispered to me. Was close. Cared. Did not send me away. I cried because she let me cry. She was gone when I woke next morning. She did not return the following night and I wondered whether I had dreamt being with her.

On the market place there was activity. The patients in the ward were excited. I stood by the window and reported to

210

Paul, "I am sure they are leaving. The Germans are leaving. Can you hear the rumbling of the armoured cars? Lorries full of soldiers are driving away. Columns are assembling. They are marching away. No, I don't know where to. The flag is coming down, Paul. The swastika is coming down. There is no flag now on top of the town hall."

Then we were told: "The Russians are on the way. The Russians will take over the occupation of Wegrow."

"Paul, a car. A soldier in a strange uniform is getting out. Another. They must be officers, they are wearing medals. And now, you won't believe it, but it is true, two German officers are coming out of the town hall . . . Paul, the world has gone mad, the Germans are facing the Russians, they salute each other, now they are going back, all four of them, they are going back into the town hall . . . another flag is going up, no, I am not imagining things, a red flag, now it is unfolding, a hammer and sickle . . . now the German officers are coming out again, they are getting into a car, they are driving away . . . Paul the Russians are here. We are safe. We are safe, Paul."

But next day, early morning, when I looked out, the swastika was flying again and German soldiers were parading outside the town hall.

"I thought it was too good to be true," said Paul. "The Germans will never give up any territory to the Russians. The Nazis and the Bolshevics trading with each other? It's crazy. A Nazi saluting a Communist. And why should the Russians come this way? Poland is not at war with Russia."

But, of course, it was true, as we learnt later. An agreement had been made between Germany and Russia. The east of Poland was to be occupied by the Russians. Where the demarcation line was to be drawn, was being negotiated at that moment. Was Wegrow to remain on the German side? How far would the Russians go?

Flags were once more exchanged the following day. But it was rumoured that the Russians might have to withdraw. We were advised to walk as soon as possible to Sokolow, about ten kilometres away. Someone gave us the address of a dentist who lived there.

"When you get there, go and see him."

We spent our last night at the hospital together in the corner of the corridor. The door behind, leading to my secret room had been locked. Someone else slept in Paul's bed.

"How do you feel, Paul?"

"It is more comfortable in a bed. As you know yourself. I felt guilty when you were lying here during those first nights. How relieved I was when you told me you had found somewhere else to sleep. I know it isn't really important, after what we have gone through, whether we sleep on a mattress or not. But trivialities do matter, nevertheless."

"Like food. But food is not trivial. I can think of eating."

"So can I. In spite of my illness. I am getting better, by the way."

"I never knew how little food one needs, Paul. We haven't had much to eat during the past weeks. And even here, we can't say we have had a lot."

"Let me tell you, as a former medical student, that the lack of food makes the stomach actually shrink. One does not feel pangs of hunger after a time."

"But I am dreaming about food, day and night, I am dreaming about it.

"You were always more interested in what there was to eat than I, Martin. Even when you were a boy, you enjoyed eating so much, that I wondered sometimes whether you would ever be interested in anything else. One always knew where to find you when you were not about."

"Find me? Where?"

"In the kitchen, of course. You spent a lot of time there."

"Not just because of the cooking, Paul. I liked to be with the servants I did not have to pretend in front of them."

"Pretend?"

"I did not have to pretend that I was as clever as you, pretend to read or to study."

"But nobody made you do those things, Martin. Nobody forced learning down your throat."

"But I wanted to be like you, don't you see? I wanted to be good at lessons, I wanted to be able to play the piano, to talk about serious matters, about capital punishment or

Wagner's operas, as you did."

"To be over four years younger makes a difference."

"Yes, Paul. Oh, how I looked up to you. I wanted to be like you. But I was bright enough to know that I could never be like you."

"And now the situation is the other way round."

"Why? I have written some poems, but they will never be as beautiful as yours. I am trying to forget that you are a real poet. I have never talked to you about your poems, only about mine sometimes. Because I'm jealous. I don't really want you to write poems. Mother said once, when she saw me scribbling, that I was only aping my big brother. Perhaps she was right. But then I do like to read now and listen to good music. And you *are* my big brother, older not just in years, that isn't so important, but you are more knowledgeable, more mature, have more insight . . . "

"Stop it, Martin, please stop it. Tell me, where would I have got to without you? Who has held me, held us both together? Whose faith has brought us so far that there is now a chance for us to survive the war? Was it I with my knowledge, my so-called intelligence, my appreciation of the arts, my learning from books, who sustained us? Or was it you who carried us both with your special brand of strength?"

"So we need each other."

"People always need each other."

"And you came back to the prison camp. You returned."

"And what would I have done without you? When I was lying in the synagogue that night, I thought I heard you calling me. I also knew I could not manage on my own. When I came back, you had already contacted that odd group of young men and it was because of you that, through them, we were freed. There is much which defies explanation. Good night, little brother."

"Good night, big brother."

On the way to Sokolow we talked a lot about hot, thick, German soups, fresh crisp rolls with jam, yeast dumplings with powidel (a sauce made out of prunes) fricassee of chicken with rice, peas and asparagus, apple tart and a special cake

213

sprinkled with almonds, beefsteaks with fried potatoes, cold meats and rings of boiling sausages, and cheeses — which Paul liked — the soft and veined ones and those with very strong smells, venison, which we had tasted very rarely, and pork and sauerkraut (the dish always prepared when our washerwoman came to the house every two weeks), chocolate mousse with whipped cream (Paul had always hated cream), oatmeal soup (my breakfast dish when I was a child), rye bread with pork dripping, the meal on Sunday — loin of veal with mixed vegetables, or on special occasions, roast goose with red cabbage — (my father asked grandfather, "Would you like a little more?" Grandfather replied, "Just a little, Leo," and father, for fun, put on the plate an almost invisible piece of meat), fruit loaf and around Easter, Matzo and honey, heaps of sandwiches, (Paul asked the cook in the evening, "Are the parents expected home? No? Please make me four sandwiches, little butter and lots of cold meat or cheese." Then he went to bed very early and ate them while listening to the radio through his headphones), potato dumplings with stewed apples, noodles cooked in milk until all the milk has been absorbed.

We talked about food until our stomachs ached and then we sat on a milestone and crunched some apples and a few hard biscuits which we had been given at the hospital. Paul spotted something shiny lying by the road. He picked it up.

"A tin of sardines, I think," he said, "the little key is still attached. I don't like fish of any sort but in these special circumstances . . . "

"It's red. It could be salmon," I said, "let's imagine it is salmon."

Paul divided the contents into two equal portions. It had always been his task to share out any food we had come by.

"I think this must be the first fish I have eaten for I don't know how many years," he said, "I have always been a terrible eater, fussy, finicky, picking at my food. Well, the parents thought I should be taught a lesson. When I was four or five, I had to have my tonsils out. The parents had had a word with the clinic staff. This, they thought, would be a good opportunity to teach the boy to eat. At first they

214

gave me plenty of ice cream. That suited me. But after a day or two when I expected to go home, I was kept in the clinic and I was given all the things I did not like: butter and cream and milk and carrots and tomatoes and cabbage. Mother must have thought my life was at risk unless I ate the right foods. I must have given the people who looked after me a bad time. Mother had to take me home soon. She told me later that I screamed so much that the staff refused to continue torturing me. But there you are. Success at last: I am eating tinned salmon."

"Better than dry biscuits."

"It is not at all bad. Mind, I would give anything for a cheese sandwich."

We had no difficulty in finding the dentist. He was a young man with a sad but caring face. He told us that the Russians were about to withdraw from Sokolow. The new border between German and Russian occupied Poland had been agreed on. The River Bug would form the frontier. If we wanted to flee from the Germans, we had to walk another thirty kilometres to get to Drohiezyn, which was on the other side of the river. There we would be safe.

We walked on. After an hour we came to a field on which lay bespattered, corpses of horses, enormous amounts of equipment, kit-bags, soldiers clothing and . . . food, plenty of it.

It must have been a strange sight to see two very young men walking through the wreckage of what must have been a battlefield, or at least a place where two armies had met, picking up apples and bread and tins, carefully climbing over the cadavers, examining boxes. ("Don't touch what looks like ammunition," called out Paul.) 'A fool's paradise,' thought Martin.

Paul put on a woolly cap and Martin laughed when he saw his brother wearing it.

"It is as unreal as anything we have seen so far," said Martin.

"Perhaps a whole Polish battalion had to surrender to the Russians here," said Paul, "these are the left-overs."

"But all these sweetly stinking horses."

"Another puzzle we cannot solve."

"Here is some smoked fat bacon," said Martin, "we talked about food all morning and now it is provided. Manna from heaven, so to speak."

"We must eat slowly," Paul said, "otherwise we shall fall ill. I have got to be particularly careful."

"I know now we shall be all right, Paul. I have had these dreadful doubts. But somehow I knew we would be safe."

"We are further away from England than before. When we have crossed the Bug we shall be in Russia. It will not be possible to get in touch with the parents from there."

"Perhaps we can let the parents know through the Red Cross that we are safe. The war can't last forever. We shall see them after the war."

"There you go again. You don't give up. You'll never give up, Martin."

"Let's go over there to the trees, Martin. We can eat and sleep. We can't make it today to the river, anyway. And we are, for once, not in a hurry. The frontier won't be closed tonight. My legs can't carry me any longer."

"I think you managed very well, Paul. After lying in bed for a week. But then you were always the better walker of us two. Father said so when we were climbing the Silesian mountains."

When they had settled down, Martin said:

"This time we won't see any German tanks coming towards us."

"We can't be quite sure."

"We shall have to decide what to do next."

"Let's leave decisions until tomorrow."

"How still everything is."

"We have become calmer."

Early next morning a slight mist hung over the landscape. Martin was awakened by Paul who recited some lines from a poem by Claudius:

216

"The forest stands out black and in silence,
    and from the meadows is rising
    the white mist miraculously."

Paul cut the bread and divided up the raw bacon. After the meal they were on their way. The Russian soldiers did not stop them from crossing the river. They found a small synagogue where they could rest and stay overnight. A small group of men were in deep conversation.

"Come and join us," someone called out. He looked like a student. His dark-rimmed glasses fell forward on his nose. He addressed the brothers and the three or four others who had settled around him with serious expressions on their faces.

"Comrades," the student said, "We are now in Russia. Because, make no mistake, the Russians will never return this piece of land to the Poles. The revolution has started in Europe. This is indeed a historic occasion. Communism is spreading. We are fortunate enough to be the first to be chosen outside the Soviet Republic, who will benefit from the new order, the order of the proletariate. This is the regime of the workers, this is our regime. Russia cares about us. Stalin cares. He knows what we Jews in Poland have suffered. The Poles spat upon us, they damaged our homes, they beat us up. Don't let's take our revenge on them. It is easy to go out on the streets now and shout: What you have done we shall do to you. We communists do not believe in what is said in the Old Testament: 'an eye for an eye'. Our slogan is 'workers' unite', all workers, Poles and Germans, Russians and Jews. This is what communism is about. Let's do away with nationalities, communism is international. The working class must act jointly to fight those who oppress us. Now we are in the position to do so. The system of capitalism is coming to an end."

He had spoken in Yiddish, but the brothers had understood what his speech was about. Now he turned to Paul and asked:

"Where do *you* come from, comrades?"

Paul told him in German.

"What were you doing before you left Czechoslovakia?"

Paul informed him.

217

k

"A medical student? You are wanted, you are wanted badly. Moscow is waiting for you. They are in need of doctors. We are all in need of doctors. You must immediately report to a Russian Officer and tell him that you have been a medical student in Prague, and that you want to complete your studies in order to serve the people. I can promise you that arrangements will be made quickly for you to go to Moscow where you will be able to go to University without having to pay any fees. You will, of course, be given an allowance. I don't think you know how fortunate you are. How I envy you. I studied law. But it is the law of the capitalists and is of no use any more. But being a doctor, that is a different matter. You must act, act without delay."

Paul turned to Martin and said:

"I'm not leaving my brother."

"Of course," was the reply, "that is understandable in the circumstances. What has he been trained in?"

Martin replied that he had had no training. He thought it best not to mention his efforts in carpentry.

"That is not so good," said the student shaking his head. "But I don't think this will make much difference. I am sure he will be permitted to go with you. He will be trained to do something useful in Russia. They need people working on the land. How lucky you are. You will be walking in Red Square before any of us."

"It sounds too good to be true," said Martin to Paul, "just imagine — you would be given the opportunity to do what you want to do."

"Are you out of your mind, Martin? In Russia. I don't think you realise what this means."

"Well, it means you will become a doctor."

"It also means that I have to cut myself off from everything which is of value to me."

"Such as?"

"Everything which is of importance to me. West European literature, music, the arts. More than that. Freedom to think. I don't want to live in a communist state. You know that I believe the individual is more important than the society he lives in. I could never live in a country where one is the servant of the state."

218

"But Paul, look at our position. It will be very difficult for us to find work, any kind of work. You won't be able to use your talents. You have completed half your studies. It would be such a waste to let it all go. If there is an opportunity for you to carry on, take it. There is music and literature in Russia and being a qualified doctor will make you feel free wherever you are."

"Do you want to come to Russia?"

"If you go, of course."

"They may not allow you to come with me."

"Well, if they don't, I shall keep my head above water somehow and visit you in Moscow as soon as I can."

"What about the parents? What about your belief that we shall be reunited?"

"I am sure the parents would be happy, very happy, if they knew you could finish your studies."

"And you, Martin, you would be happy?"

"Oh, I would miss you Paul, miss you very much, if I had to stay behind."

The next day the subject was not discussed any more.

The brothers heard they could have a bath in a side-street, not far from the synagogue. They had not had one since they had left Kattowitz.

We thought that the mikvah was a community bath for Jews. We did not know then that a mikvah is a bath for Jewish women who, according to Jewish law, are required to bathe at the end of their monthly period or after bearing a child. Of course, we were ignorant of this particular ritual, but no one stopped us from undressing and handing in our clothes, which were put into a large drum for fumigation. We entered the wash-house, which smelt like the cloakroom next to the gym in our school. There were buckets of hot water and also some evil-smelling soap. It was strange to see Paul naked. I did not think I had seen him without clothes since we were both children. Here he stood in front of me, his intimate, careworn face now becoming smooth and almost relaxed; and I knew so well the wiry arms through which the veins shone and the hands with their long fingers, which seemed to be, even during our wanderings, free from grime, unlike mine. But his chest, stomach, abdomen, genitals, knees, legs, toes, his shoulders, back, bottom: they were like those of any stranger. Here was I, facing him whom I loved, who had a body which was unfamiliar to me, here was he, so close but also alien. How little I knew about him whom I loved. His gestures, his speech had become part of me, but there was so much else I knew nothing about. I only knew what he willingly revealed. So much remained concealed, concealed even from me with whom he slept under his coat.

We had both despaired and hoped and had lost hope and had endured. Some of our experiences had been terrifying. I knew then, in the dampness of the wash-room, that it is not possible to go on living with such intensity. And the 'day would come', when Paul would live outside me. I should be on my own then.

I had no right to look at his body, as I had no right to look into the inside of him. I looked away. I had no right to discover what he did not want me to discover.

There will be the time when we shall both walk in different directions. Already I dreaded the loss.

We threw cool water over ourselves.

I shivered a little.

The brothers reasoned that it would perhaps be possible to find work in a large town and they left Drohiezyn in good spirits. After a while a Russian army lorry stopped and they were given a lift. Somebody mentioned Bialystok, a large Polish city now occupied by the Russians. At a small railway station they got off. They had been told that trains to Bialystok were passing through here. They had to wait a very long time. Then a train steamed in and halted. Tickets were not needed. They found two vacant seats and when it became dark they leaned on each other and fell asleep.

The brothers woke up in the middle of the night. The other passengers were talking loudly. They gathered that this train was not going to Bialystok after all.

"If you want to get to Bialystok, you must get off here and take another train."

"Where is this train going to?"

"It is going to Wilna."

"Is Wilna as large as Bialystok?"

"Larger, much larger."

The brothers looked at each other. It did not really matter whether the place was called Bialystok or Wilna, as long as it was big enough for them to find work.

They decided to stay on the train.

IV

ARRIVALS

We got off the train in Wilna on the fifth of October and stayed for the next five months.

Recently I found a small map of the city in a book on the Soviet Union. It brought back no memories. I could not recognise any familiar landmarks. No doubt, during the past forty years, the city has been completely rebuilt. Still, this does not explain why I cannot even remember the river which winds itself around the city and runs through the centre. Nor can I recall historic buildings described in the book and marked on the map: churches founded in the 15th and 16th century, or the remains of a castle overlooking the city, or the apparently often restored and reconstructed cathedral, which dates from the 14th century. I must have passed them many times and looked at them. I have to remind myself that Vilnius, the capital of the Lithuanian Soviet Socialist Republic, was Wilna, occupied by the Russians, when Paul and I arrived there after five weeks of wild wandering in Poland.

We did not travel to Bialystok. This would have meant that we had to get out of the train and wait for another. But Paul and I wanted nothing but to be left alone and rest. Our lassitude resulted in our eventual arrival in England.

Many years ago Paul gave me for my birthday, a little book of photographs which he got from one of the second-hand

222

bookshops in the West End. *A Ghetto in the East (Wilna)*. The beautiful and evocative pictures were taken between the two world wars and these mean much to me. This is the Wilna we knew: narrow lanes and alleys, cobblestones, temples and small prayer houses, iron gateways and court- yards, houses nearly collapsing under the weight of their age, shop windows with shutters closed, dingy corners, puddles, roofs which almost touch each other, tiny windows, grey and brown walls, archways, damp cellars, almost darkness even in the mornings. I can smell the smell of poverty, the unwashed clothes, the excrements. I can see the people in their ill-fitting clothes with caps and shawls, the men often bearded, the wrinkled faces of women holding their hands folded in front of them. There must have been children. There are no pictures of children in my mind. There is the market, many markets where everything is sold, mostly useless items, sold or exchanged: trousers with patches, jackets with their seams unstitched, shoes with a heel missing, even a pair of underpants is held up for show.

Crowds of Poles and Jews are milling around bartering, agitated, picking up this and that, a woollen scarf, a pair of mittens, a fur cap. (Frau Seeliger would have been in her element here.) Russian soldiers are looking for watches and clocks and do not care about their condition, as long as they tick. Money is losing its value, zloties are changed into roubles at a poor rate. Tobacco is very precious, cigarettes are long and slender but only the tips are lightly stuffed with tobacco. For ten of these you will have to pay a heavy price in cash or goods.

We bought whatever could be eaten with the money we still had not spent. At the beginning of our stay, bread and apples were our staple food. I had already learnt from Frau Seeliger how to haggle and often I got apples for much less than was asked for. Sometimes I stole. Paul was embarrassed and turned away.

For bread, we had to queue very early in the mornings. The loaves, probably a mixture of various cereals, were still warm when we bought them. Crisp outside, but sticky and half raw inside. One could easily change the bread back into dough again by rolling pieces in one's mouth. Bread

223

became clay. Paul and I ate it immediately, the warm gooey mass, we broke the bread and ate it, still in front of the bakers', in the street, walking away, gulping it down, in spite of the ache we knew we would have shortly.

I don't know who told us to go to that little café in one of the thread-like lanes in the Jewish quarter. You go there, we were told, there are good people there. We went in and sat down in the corner by the window and when the good woman came and asked us what we wanted, we shrugged our shoulders and turned out our empty pockets. (Paul kept the few coins we still had in a safe place.) When she had served the other customers, she brought us barley soup. And then there was tea, hot red liquid in glasses which we drank sucking a sweet at the same time. We went back to the café whenever we were hungry and often had to wait until early afternoon when she gave us barley soup or cabbage soup or sometimes meat-balls. We never left the café without getting something to eat. She never asked for money.

As a former medical student Paul was later given a meal voucher. This we used in turn. Lunch in a private house. It was the same menu — you could not get anything else to eat in Wilna then — barley soup, or cabbage soup, meat-balls, apples and tea. One had to wait outside the dining-room — the professional 'guests', suitably attired, were in deep conversation, but there were no aperitifs — then the door opened and we went in, sat down at a table covered with white tablecloth, the silvery cutlery glittered, and the waitress with a starched cap and shining apron served us with a smile: cabbage soup, or on alternate days, barley soup and on occasions meat-balls. We did not belong here and after a few times we decided not to take advantage of this free meal and to go back to the café where we could have our meal together and where we would feel at ease.

We went to the refugee centre and registered. We were relieved that we were not the only ones who had found their way to Wilna. There were scores of refugees — how many we did not know – and some had even found accommodation. We met an acquaintance of Paul's. Winkler had been a fellow-student in Paul's faculty in Prague. But they had never been close. In fact, there had been some animosity between them. Winkler had been keen on Rita, Paul's beautiful girlfriend.

"He bore a grudge against me," said Paul later, "but I was not prepared to give up Rita. We quarrelled. He accused me of being possessive."

Winkler appeared to have forgotten all about it.

"Some of us are staying in rooms," he said, "where do you live?"

Paul replied that we were sleeping in halls, schools and any other place which gave shelter. It was certainly uncomfortable, but we had got used to sleeping on sheets of newspaper.

"Well, there may be a chance, just a chance, for you to join us," Winkler said, "all the beds are occupied, I'm sorry to say, but there might be some space on the floor."

I wanted again to belong to a group, any group. Paul and I would not depend on each other all day long, I thought, one could talk to others, do little tasks like cleaning the room. If there was a leader – there is always a leader – he would act for us. Decisions would be made for us, one would become part of an organisation, in a group one would find one's identity.

Winkler said he would have a word with the others. Paul said that Winkler was the last person he would have thought of asking for something. Anyhow, he didn't think that Winkler would do anything for us.

But the next day Winkler confirmed that we could move in. We could sleep on the floor by the window. We went to the place immediately. Men were sitting on their beds, looking at us with suspicion. Their belongings were spread out on the beds or hanging on strings above the beds, cases had been stacked underneath. The men looked as if they were prepared to defend their territories. Perhaps they were worried that we would start a fight with them, throw out their things and occupy the beds. But we spread out Paul's coat on the floor. We were not on our own any more. Later someone brought us some blankets. We had found a home.

A day or two later Winkler asked us to see a doctor. We asked him why, neither of us was ill, did all the residents see a doctor when they moved in? Winkler shrugged his shoulders.

The doctor, a refugee who lived somewhere else, made us strip, looked at us and said: "You are suffering from the same complaint as the rest of us. You were asked to come and see me because you have been seen scratching yourselves a great deal. Your room-mates were worried in case you were suffering from some kind of infection, like scabies. But you aren't. You are lousy. You understand? Pediculosis. Infested with lice, like we all are. No need to worry. It's nothing worse than lice. They will tell you what to do about it."

When we went back and told them, they laughed. They told us to take off our shirts. Then they showed us how to look, in the light, at the seams and squash them one by one.

This was more than I could take. Lice. The extreme degradation. It had come to this. Lousy. Filthy. Dirty. I broke down. Parasites feeding on me. Like the bedbugs when I was little. Tears were flowing. Paul looked at me, helpless. He tried to make light of the matter. But it was not easy to console me. We could not sink any lower. They lay eggs and there are more lice and more and they suck you dry until there is nothing left of you. Lice have taken us over. All our suffering has been for nothing. Please God, let me die.

It was not easy to get rid of them. Paul became an expert in killing them and did not mind going through my shirt. A few weeks later we were free of lice.

We did not pay any rent. We understood that a committee had been formed which was responsible for all the financial arrangements. We did not ask questions. We were glad to be members of the group. But one day we were told that more refugees had arrived and that the space by the window was needed for new people. Would we mind moving into a hotel? The committee would see to it that the bills were paid. A hotel? Hardly that. It was a dingy place, two or three kilometres away. But the arrangement would only be a temporary one. As soon as there were any vacant beds — people tried to find their own accommodation — we would be the first ones to whom they would be offered. We could still come back, of course, and visit the others.

The hotel was a cheap lodging house. The smell of cabbage hit you as soon as you stepped into the lobby. The coarse unkempt woman who showed us the room, looked as I imagined a brothel-keeper to look. Our room with the double bed was so dark that it was necessary to turn the light on, although it was only after lunch when we moved in. The furniture was shabby, but the bed was large and soft and it was heaven to lie between sheets once more. But we were lonely, away from the others. We tried to joke.

"You can't bring a girl here," said Paul, "I need my rest."

"Yes, it's too cold now for you to find a bench," I replied.

"Now, if you were on your own, that would be a different matter."

The proprietress solved the problem for herself.

One afternoon when we came back rather earlier than usual, we were just about to open the door to our room — the rooms were not lockable — when we heard voices coming from inside.

"Who is there?" called Paul.

Silence. Then loud laughter. Laughter from a couple.

A man's voice: "Go away, we are in bed."

We went to find the hotel-keeper.

"They must leave," said Paul, "we want to get into our rooms."

"Bad times," she said, "a few extra zloties make a lot of difference."

Walking outside with Paul, hoping for the early departure of the couple, I gave vent to my feelings of indignation. Paul took it philosophically.

"It's nothing to be so shocked about," he said, "it happens all over the world."

"What? That your room is let out when you happen to be away?"

"You are still very young, little brother."

When we went to our room later, we saw that the sheets had not been changed. The bed was not even made.

My suppressed aggression broke out like a dog which had been kept too long on a lead. As in the prison in Lublin, when I had lost my temper with a fellow prisoner for spitting on the cell floor, my prudish upbringing, my intolerance, my uppishness got the better of me.

"You are as filthy as you look," I shouted at the hotel-keeper, "it is bad enough to live here in this pigsty, but we don't have to put up with your afternoon trade. Go and change the sheets at once. We are not going to sleep in other people's dirty linen."

She did not say anything in reply. Probably she only understood half of what I blurted out.

"How odd," said Paul when we were lying in bed, the fresh sheets still damp.

"Odd? What is odd?"

"Matters which become quite unimportant in particular situations, become important again when the circumstances change."

I did not pretend that I did not know what he was referring to.

Paul went on, "Would you have minded so much, only a few weeks ago whether anybody had slept in your bed or made love in it? I know you are particular about some things. We are all fastidious about certain things and not about others. And yet, wasn't your reaction out of proportion to the event?"

"You can't say, can you, that it is proper to treat guests in the way she did?"

"Guests? What guests? We are not guests? We are refugees. A low category of people. Refugees who have been given a bed for free. The committee, whatever that means, probably only pays her a petty amount for this room."

"But Paul, you would not have slept in the dirty sheets."

"No, I would not. That is not the point. It is your anger, your impetuosity, your lack of self-discipline, I am concerned about."

"Yes, I was angry."

"You were shouting at the woman in the corridor."

"I did not mean it to be a secret."

"You put yourself on her level. You made yourself cheap. You have no right to call somebody filthy."

"She is filthy."

228

"By abusing her you abused yourself."

"All right, big brother. The lesson is over. I am as filthy as she is. And anyhow, the whole thing is quite unimportant. Soiled sheets are no subject for the intelligentsia."

I thought I knew how to hurt him. It was our first quarrel since we had set out from Kattowitz. I slept badly that night.

Next day Paul's illness started.

It was a kind of migraine. The pains were so severe at times that he could not talk. He only whispered. Even the dim light from the yard finding its way through the dirt-caked window, hurt his eyes. The grey curtains had to remain closed. I asked the doctor, the same who diagnosed our skin condition, to come and see him. Being a refugee, he was not in a position to prescribe any drugs. But Paul did not want to be treated by anyone else. The doctor looked into Paul's eyes. Reflexes appeared to be normal. His temperature was normal. There were no other symptoms apart from the excruciating pain. The doctor asked me whether I could bring Paul a hot meal every day. I said that I would collect it from the soup kitchen. The doctor said that Paul was suffering from exhaustion and that he needed rest and care. He did not think there was anything organically wrong.

I blamed myself. I was certain that it was the quarrel which had triggered off Paul's illness. I would try to make it up to him somehow.

I walked through the crowded streets, carrying two pots with soup and the well-known meat-balls. Oh, why had I not kept quiet? I had known that he was right. I, with my self-importance and arrogance. And my obvious need to be cruel to others. What did I care about that stupid, shameless, slattern. I had hurt Paul. Hurt him so much that his head cannot shake off the hurt. I don't deserve him. He might die. I have pushed him away and now I cannot have him back. I have lost him.

One day he whispered to me that it would be nice if I could read to him. Perhaps I could get hold of a German book? I said that I would get one from somewhere. There was no point in asking our new friends whether they had books in German. These would have probably been lost during their escapes. What about the libraries?

The city library would not lend books to a refugee and the Jewish library only had books in Hebrew and Yiddish. But I spotted, not far from the lodging house, a small shop where books were overflowing the shelves or lying in large heaps on the floor. There was a small section of German books. I could not possibly read to Paul *Walking through the Black Forest*, or *Anna's Downfall* (pub. 1897), or *Minor Poets of the 18th Century* (1912), or *Important Sermons* (a handbook for communicants). But I could not go back with empty hands. Was there nothing, nothing at all which Paul would enjoy? I found it. Dickens' *Christmas Books* in a German translation.

I pushed the rickety chair near the window and opened the curtain just enough for the light to show the yellowish pages of the book. Paul lay on his back, the blanket drawn up to his chin. His eyes were closed. It was the face of an old man. He, my brother, my big brother, so much older than I, an old man with an ashen face, a stubble of reddish hair on his cheeks. What has been done to him, I thought, what have I done to him? Please make him better, make him better for me. I know I am selfish, but I cannot be without him, I need him. I am willing to take his place, I am not important, I can bear his pain but I can't bear to see him like this. I can't bear it.

I started to read: "The Battle of Life. A love Story."

Paul whispered: "Surely this is not the story about Scrooge?"

"No, there are several stories in this book. The Christmas Carol is another one. Would you prefer me to read that one?"

"No. It doesn't matter."

"The Battle of Life. A Love Story. 'Once upon a time, it matters little when, and in stalwart England, it matters little where, a fierce battle was fought. It was fought upon a long summer day when the waving grass was green. Many a wild flower, formed by the Almighty Hand to be a perfumed goblet for the dew, felt its enamelled cup filled high with blood that day and shrinking, dropped. Many an insect

230

deriving its delicate colour from harmless leaves and herbs, was stained anew that day by dying men and marked its frightened way with an unnatural track. The painted butterfly took blood into the air upon the edges of its wings. The stream ran red. The trodden ground became a quagmire, when from sudden pools collected in the prints of human feet and horses hoofs, the one prevailing hue still lowered and glimmered in the sun.' "

Paul tried to lift himself up but he fell back. He spoke quietly and clearly, there was no whispering:

"What an extraordinary writer Dickens was. What a picture in words he's painting here."

I said that I could not remember any description like this in *Oliver Twist*, one of the few books by Dickens which I had read.

"He was a critic of English society and he was often sentimental," said Paul.

"And funny," I added.

"Yes, and funny. But then you come across a passage like this, full of wonder."

"It could be a picture of the last judgement."

"But it also depicts something you and I can recognise, can't we, Martin?"

Paul smiled, ruefully and sadly, but he smiled.

One of the first things we had to do when Paul was feeling better, was to go to the barber. We had no shaving kit and Paul's sprouting face looked a mess. Although most shops were closed, the barber in the Jewish quarter was always in business. Paul counted the coins and thought there was enough left to pay him, but the barber did not want any money from us. On the contrary. While Paul was sitting in the chair – like a doctor, I thought, with a white apron – there was a collection. Waiting customers put coins and notes into a cap which was passed on from hand to hand. I blushed. I wanted to shout out that we were not beggars. But I pretended not to notice.

Paul was not disconcerted when he put the stack of money into his pocket. When we left the shop, he said:

"Surely, they can afford it."

But the large contribution which the people in the barber's shop had made was of little value. Polish zloties were becoming worthless. The currency was now Russian roubles.

"They must have known it," I said to Paul, "they made fun of us."

"Perhaps," replied Paul, "but it must be a marvellous feeling to be able to give, even if one knows that there is little point in doing so."

"It is dishonest," I replied.

"For you, everything is either white or black, good or bad, honest or dishonest, Martin. Don't be so intolerant. I'm sure they thought we could do something with the money. And we can. Cinemas still accept zloties."

I have already told you that going to the cinema had become almost a necessity. It was one way to escape the grimness of the day. In Kattowitz, Paul and I had seen many American films (with Polish subtitles) which were so severely cut, that it was often impossible to follow the story, even if our English had been better than it was. A feature film never lasted longer than one hour and we could see two or three films in one programme. In Wilna it was different, of course. All films were Russian, most of them old and silent, with a political message. Often they were beautiful to look at and it was not too difficult to follow the plot. We also thought, as we were practically in Soviet Russia, the films would help us in our understanding of socialism. We saw Eisenstein's *October* and *Strike*, Dovzhenko's *Earth* and Pudowkin's *Mother*. *Mother* particularly, moved me strangely, I remember.

To go to the cinema was not merely to have somewhere to stay, but it was something 'normal' to do, something we had always done, a link between then and now, a bridge between the past and the present.

A few weeks later, when we had a little money, we went to one or two concerts and once even to the *Bartered*

Bride performed by a Lithuanian opera company which had travelled to Wilna from Kaunas. It was a strange version of this famous Czech folk opera which we had both seen performed in Prague. We could not help giggling. Music was one of Paul's passions and his love became also my love. We stood somewhere at the back of the hall and Paul whispered comments or explanations into my ear. He was happy and resembled the brother I remembered from before our journey.

'So much has happened in such a short time,' I thought, 'shall I be able to carry it?'

*   *   *   *

The last day in Breslau. I was to travel the next day to Prague to be with Paul until the parents arrived in a few weeks. I was very excited. My passport showed an entry: 'one month vacation trip', but it was planned that I should not return. I was to be with Paul, staying in his room near the enormous Wenzel Square not far from the University.

A new start. Away from the parents. Away from the flat which had become hateful to me. Away from Breslau. Away from Germany where we Jews had no place any more. To be with Paul, my big brother, who had made a life for himself, away from us, away from it all.

But it had irked me to have to leave my first employment as a commercial apprentice in a travel bureau just when Richard, the trainee, had been made an apprentice himself.

Blond, good-looking Richard had sent me on messages last year. As a trainee he did not receive any wages. He thought he was my superior. I resented fetching and carrying for him. I could not get rid of the suspicion that people took advantage of my good-heartedness, my lack of wit, my ugliness. Richard's behaviour towards me upset me to such a degree, that father finally agreed to go and see the manager who — credit to him — understood the situation. From the beginning of this year, Richard had started his apprenticeship and I was his senior. I was not to enjoy my elevated position for long. I left the bureau at the end of February 1937, a few days before my departure to Prague. Richard would be on his

233

own. There was no Martin Rosen to tell him to get on with the filing of the letters.

Such a trivial episode. But it still sticks in my mind as an important event. What a child I am still.

Breslau in winter. Deep snow. Silent afternoons. I am sitting too well wrapped up on the sledge. Somebody is pulling it, not Paul, probably a servant. I close my eyes. Moving forward with little pulls. Only the slight rustling sound of the snow underneath.

When I was older I skated on the iced-up tennis court. Never good at it, I was usually dragging a foot. A lame man on ice. Late in the day, when most skaters had left, there was freedom from one corner to the other. Music from the loudspeakers: 'Vienna, Vienna, only you are the city of my dreams.' I did not dance on the ice, I could not. It was the lilt, the lilt that lifted me.

It was very, very cold. Christmas holidays had been extended because of the cold. Shortage of coal, it was said. Unexpected pleasure. Playing by myself in the overheated room. Submitting to the whims of Paula, the beautiful child who played the violin so sweetly that tears came into the eyes of the grown-ups. Paula lived in the flat opposite to ours and we played together on many wintry days. She ordered me about, and I let her. She chose the games and I agreed to whatever she proposed. Once she made me take my trousers down and then ran to Paul and complained that I had been rude. When some toy got broken she called her mother and pointed at me. Yet, I went back and asked her to play with me. I loved to look at her. I asked her whether she would marry me. She was in front of me, above me, on the flight of stairs leading to our flats. She stood still and turned round slowly. Looking down at me, I can still hear her: "You, Martin? Marry you? You're not handsome enough for me." Of course, she was right, but I did not want to play with her any more. And I didn't.

Breslau in spring. Melting snow: the white-brown mess. I pulled down my long woollen stockings. (Mother must not know.) There was promise around me. Promise in the wind

234

which brushed against me. The trees in the South Park began to speak. Blossoms blinded me. Going for walks alone and later with Georg, to the Round Tower or to the end of the city, to the railway bridge where we counted the carriages of the ever rumbling freight trains, or into the fields, with the carpet of deep brown soil. Hope without reason. All would be easier from now on. Summer was waiting to burst upon me. The school year would finish at Easter. I shall try harder in the new class. Please, let me not repeat the year. A nightmare: The horse chestnuts are falling from the trees and break open and show their chocolate ripeness. No, not autumn yet. Not yet, please.

Breslau in summer. Swimming. A feeling of strength. I am succeeding, I am winning. The water belonged to me, especially in the deep and where there were not many people. Trips by tram to the cemetery with grandfather. School outings when it was sunny and mother permitted. The boat along the Oder through the locks. Or by the little train to Trebnitz. Or to the zoo. Or to the 'Hall of the Century', (its roundness was incredible). The lilac in the house. The walk, sometimes with the parents, to the café 'Garden Beauty' (apple juice and a meringue with whipped cream). Long holidays to come. Where shall we go this year? Rides on my cycle. Perhaps I shall discover a place where there will be nobody but me. There I will lie in the grass and look into the sky and watch how the clouds changed their shapes.

Breslau in autumn. The noisy mat of coloured leaves. In the parks, the squares, even in our small neglected garden. My shoes have become shovels. My kites never flew. I carried them with such care to the 'Kinder Zobten' but the wind never lifted them up. The body was too heavy, the tail too short. If only the wind would lift me up, right up, across the roof of the houses, away from home, from school, from the dark evenings. There death was waiting. I wanted to escape. My Latin efforts were so poor. There was no excuse for me to go out and play in the streets. Blustering rain. Paul insisted that I should do my homework. "Ciconia – the stork, rana – the frog. Ciconia ranam captat. The stork is catching the frog. Is this correct, Paul?" Everything gets caught. Everything dies.

I shall take with me memories, emotions, sensations. No images of the many beautiful old churches, the cathedral, the university, the museums (which I rarely entered). No images even of the parks and squares unless they were in the vicinity of my home, nor of the islands on the river. All these I can only vaguely visualise now. Breslau (Germany) became Wroclaw (Poland) after the war.

From the brochure of the Polish Travel Office:
'In Mid-twelfth century the town began to flourish and in the times of King Boleslav the Wrymouth it continued to develop, became very rich and attracted scholars from all over Europe. In the years that followed, Wroclaw lived under the rule of Bohemian, Austrian and Prussian dynasties. But as late as the 19th century, the Polish language was spoken in Wroclaw, sermons were preached in Polish in many churches till the 18th century and Polish scientists worked at the University of Wroclaw. In the second half of the 19th century the persecution of Polish tradition started and was later continued with unquenched fury, especially in the times when Hitler came to power: the old historical names of the streets were changed and everything that provided evidence of the Slavonic past of the town was uprooted.'

I knew nothing of this when I was a child. Breslau was a German city and I was a German child.

My father told me how he had deceived a business friend from Berlin once, who had come to Breslau for a visit.

"I hope you realise," my father wrote to him, "that Breslau is a Polish city. Hardly any German is spoken here. I would advise you to bring with you a Polish phrase-book."

The friend arrived and was met at the station by a small group of people, briefed beforehand by my father. They pretended to be Poles. But only a very few Poles lived in Breslau at that time. The capital of Lower Silesia was as German as any other town in Germany. According to my father, they all went to a wine tavern in the evening and had a good laugh.

I have read that three quarters of the city was destroyed during the last weeks of the war. Only six thousand people still lived in Breslau when the war ended, many had taken refuge in the countryside and when they returned they found their houses demolished. They were directed to move away, to the west. The Poles who had been in labour camps throughout Germany and were on their way back to their homeland, moved in. Breslau offered opportunities and became a Polish city.

Breslau as I knew it, has been dead for many years. Wroclaw was in the news not long ago. Worker's demonstrations made the headlines. I read it in the papers. It meant nothing to me.

I met Georg. We went for our last walk together. He gave me a little book, carefully wrapped up.

"Don't open it now. Leave it until tomorrow when you are in the train."

"I also brought you something," I said, "it's a story I wrote specially for you. The theme is the same as I've written about before. The total immersion in nature."

"Thank you. We had so many talks about it."

"It is the ultimate experience. To become one with the tree, the meadow, the flower, to dissolve into nothing, no, not into nothing, but to recognise onself in the shape of a branch or a blade of grass and then take on its form, its soul. That must be the greatest experience a human being can have."

"But can it be achieved?"

"Perhaps not by oneself. Perhaps only with someone else. Someone one loves."

"Oh, your beautiful thoughts, Martin. Are they just beautiful? I know you so well. I love you more than anybody else. How I shall miss you."

"You must come and see me very soon. We must walk in the Czech mountains together. We must try to attain this

237

union with nature."

"You will write, won't you?"

"We shall keep close in our letters."

"You've given me so much. Not just your stories and your poems."

"Let's not say 'good-bye'. I am just turning round and leaving. You will hear from me."

"Yes, remember me to Paul."

I never saw Georg again. He was exterminated.

Then I went to see Toni.

"So you are off, you lucky chap."

"I'm travelling tomorrow."

"I envy you. To Prague. I've been there, you know, two years ago with a group of boys. Stayed at a Youth Hostel which was not too clean. Splendid place, Prague. While I have to go on swotting in school, you will be a man of leisure."

"I don't know about that. I shall have to do some secretarial work for my father. We're expecting the parents to join us in a few weeks."

"We had some good times together, didn't we, Martin? I always remember that show we produced at school. Particularly the scene from 'Midsummer Night's Dream', 'Pyramus and Thisby'. You made a splendid wall. I still laugh when I think about it."

"I remember. It's difficult to put into words how much I valued your friendship."

"Don't talk such rot. You talk in the past. Czechoslovakia is not far from here, a few hours by train, that's all. When I come to see you, I shall expect first class coffee and cream cakes."

"I shall see that you get them. Well, good-bye, Toni. Remember me to your parents."

"I shall. Cheerio, Martin."

It was the last time I saw Toni. Toni was exterminated.

In the evening we took grandfather out. We went to a variety

238

show. While watching the 'Revels' — a group of famous acrobatic clowns — I was thinking that I would be with Paul tomorrow at the same time. I could hardly contain my joy. Grandfather was sitting next to me, grandfather who had lived with us throughout my childhood. I was not sad to leave him. We had never been very intimate. And then, father had assured him that he would not have to stay behind for very long. As soon as business allowed, grandfather would come and join us.

When, next day, the parents and grandfather came with me to the station to see me off, I was so inattentive that my father had to pull me up sharply.

"Pay a little attention to grandfather. Go and talk to him."

But I could find nothing to say to him.

Later father briefed me:

"Listen, Martin. Don't forget, you're on holiday. You're a tourist. You must not tell the border guards that you're not coming back."

"Yes, I understand."

"The train is about to leave. I've put a rug in the corner seat. A wooden seat can feel quite uncomfortable on a long journey."

"Thank you."

"Go and kiss your mother and grandfather."

I went to them and embraced them. I felt nothing but happiness.

I did not see my grandfather again. It was never possible for him to join us. After the war we heard that he was spared the journey to Auschwitz. He died a natural death.

In the train I unwrapped Georg's book, read the dedication, blushed and became angry. I tore out the page but kept it.

The examination of my luggage at the border took a long time and I was afraid I would miss the train. My violin which I had brought with me was particularly scrutinised. The German border police probably suspected that some jewels had been hidden inside. What on earth made me take it along anyway? I would never be able to play like Paula. When I was little I had had some piano lessons, but I did not make any progress. Then I had the idea of learning to play the violin. I was convinced that the violin was the instrument through which I could express myself. I only had to hold it under my chin and gently move the bow over the strings, and angelic music would flow through the air. Perhaps I had a little talent. But I did not work at it. A good tone but no technique. Like my poems and the stories. My creative efforts lacked discipline and the skill of craftsmanship.

"A gift needs to be worked at, nourished, cared for, then it can be exploited," Paul had said. I never worked at anything, I did not practise the violin and I did not learn the craft of writing. Yet I was convinced I had something special to offer. There was no doubt in my mind, I was an artist.

Paul was waiting for me at the station and took me to his room. The couch was so large that we called it 'the meadow of love'. I slept lying at his feet. My happiness was immeasurable.

The next day was Paul's twenty-first birthday. I had brought my present to him with me, Jacobsen's *Mogens* (which I had read on the train) and my parents had instructed me to buy a cake. I bought a huge chocolate gateau and a bottle of wine. We celebrated in his room. Paul said he was very glad to have me staying with him. He only hoped I would not get bored. He could not afford to miss lectures. I said I was going to go for little walks, or look out of the window, or read. I was content.

I gave no thought to Breslau, the parents, grandfather, Georg, Toni. I was with Paul, nothing else mattered.

When Paul was not busy studying, he showed me something of the beautiful city. The old merged with the new. Cobblestones in side roads, but also wide modern streets. Buildings showing off their age in the old town, but also sleek contemporary constructions. And then the fairy-like castle and the Gothic cathedral.

In the evenings we went out sometimes, and Rita came with us on a few occasions. I remember performances of *Macbeth* in the German Theatre, and we saw three operas,

240

Orfeo ed Euridice, *Eugen Onegin* and the *Bartered Bride*. The audience seemed to take as much part in the production as the singers on the stage in Smetana's masterpiece. There was an air of festivity in the opera house, people hummed the well-known tunes and danced in their seats. It was an experience I shall never forget. (No wonder we could not take the Lithuanian production seriously.)

Paul introduced me to what others had created, he made me look outside, away from myself, into a world of new wonders. I entered it and have never left it.

One Sunday we walked to the river. Near the Charles Bridge we had lunch in the open, looking at the floating boats. There was thick asparagus soup (made with cream), meat in a spicy sauce and a heavy doughy pudding. The meal was not like anything I had ever had before. Paul watched me enjoying myself.

"Food still plays an important part in your life, Martin, doesn't it?"

I did not reply.

How could I put into words my great happiness: to be with him, to sleep in his room, to go out with him, to eat with him? How could I express my great love for him?

Three weeks later we received a telegram from the parents. They had arrived in Brünn and were expecting us the following day.

The end of some wonderful weeks.

Paul travelled with me to Brünn and stayed with us for a little while, until we had found accommodation with Frau Binder.

I did not visit Paul in Prague again.

*　　*　　*　　*

Two beds had become vacant in what was now called the hostel, soon after Paul's recovery. We left the 'hotel', pleased that we would be together again with the others who had accepted us as equals. A few days after our move I became ill.

My legs had become infected. Our doctor said that I needed hospital care. At first I refused to go. I did not want to leave Paul and the others. But the doctor was firm. With Paul at my arm I limped to the grey building. There was a lot of squabbling amongst the staff about whether I should be admitted. After some time we were taken to a large ward and Paul helped me to undress. I felt ashamed of my dirty clothes. Paul made a bundle of them and said that he would wash everything. I was given a long nightshirt.

'Like a shroud,' I thought, although I had never seen one.

I was very tired. As soon as Paul had left, I fell asleep. Meals interrupted my sleep: a crispy roll in the morning, soups or hash for lunch and in the evening. I had not had so much to eat for months. I felt guilty not being able to share anything with Paul.

I was injected with some milky substance. These injections were painful. The nurses probably thought I was not really ill, merely suffering from exhaustion. They treated me with a certain amount of roughness.

When Paul came, he assured me that he managed very well. He was still going to the Jewish café, he queued up every morning for bread and sometimes he cooked something for himself at the hostel. His headaches had now gone and he spent a lot of time in the library of the University, where there were a lot of German books, which he could not take out.

There was some talk that the Russians would leave Wilna and hand it over to the Lithuanians.

"Why to the Lithuanians?" I asked. "What have the Lithuanians got to do with Wilna?"

"I have been told," replied Paul, "that Wilna was once the capital of Lithuania, that it had to be handed over to Poland and that the Russians intend to return it."

"Would it make any difference to us?"

"It might. We have to wait and see."

"I want to get up now and go with you. They are not really friendly here."

"It is best you stay until they throw you out."

"I have kept a roll for you. Hide it. It is better than the bread you buy."

"Don't worry about me so much. I'm all right."

"You are certainly the stronger of us two now."

242

"You used up all your energy for both of us."

"I want to come back with you."

"I brought a pack of cards with me."

"Cards? Where did you get them from?"

"Somebody in the hostel gave them to me."

"When did we play cards the last time? Did we ever?"

Paul shuffled the cards. Then he held the pack in his hand.

"We did, Martin. You remember the so-called quiet hours in the resorts? When we were not allowed to make any noise, so as not to disturb the people having their midday rest?"

"I remember. We played snap when you did not want to read. Playing with you, permitted to play with you, those were special occasions."

"You always agreed to whatever I suggested."

"I was only too happy to do what you wanted me to do."

"I took advantage of that."

"Of course you did. You were so much older than I, but still a child. I was quite willing to drop everything I was doing when you wanted to play with me."

"We played some strange games, didn't we, Martin?"

"We made them up. Or rather, you made them up. I agreed."

"There was the game with the two tricycles, riding, no, driving along a definite route, marked out with chairs and other pieces of furniture in our two adjoining rooms. Driver Green and Driver Black."

"There must have been some purpose to the game, but I've forgotten what it was. I think I was always Driver Black."

"He was probably always the one who got into trouble with Driver Green. I was Green, of course."

"Then there were the games we sometimes played when we were both in bed and supposed to go to sleep. You in your room and I in mine, with the door wide open. We called them 'Talking Games'."

"One of those games I remember. You had to look outside the window and describe to me what the people in the house opposite were doing."

"And you made up some crazy word games which only we could possibly make sense of."

"When we made too much noise and the servant heard us,

she ran into your room and smacked you. You were always the one who was blamed."

"But, Paul, believe me, I didn't really mind. Anyhow she only hit the cushions."

"Of course, there was our model of the zoo."

"The zoo. We had hundreds of animals."

"And several large cages and dozens of fences and shrubs and trees."

"You laid it all out sometimes, when we had holidays. It took hours to do. I was your assistant."

"Of course. You had to build the enclosures exactly as I directed."

"And I had to watch the shows."

"The shows?"

"The circus performances. You tried to make the elephants stand on each other. Grandfather and I made up the audience."

"And I couldn't make the models balance properly. How could I? But then I lost my temper, smashed up everything I had prepared, the arena and all the other paraphernalia. Your older brother was not easy to live with."

"You made me unhappy at times. I wanted so much for you to be happy."

"I made use of you."

"I wanted to be used by you. You remember the parents' partics?"

"One can't forget them."

"Everything in the flat was turned upside down. Your room became the cloakroom. Grandfather had to move out for the night and stay with friends. Your bed was moved into my room. That was the greatest of all delights. I was looking forward to that night for days. We would be close. We would spend the night together."

"But often I spoilt it for you. I didn't want to play or talk. I had a headache or tummyache or some other imaginary complaint."

"But your illness didn't last longer than an hour. And then you joined in."

"What a despicable child I must have been."

"You were my big brother. You still are, of course."

244

"I always managed somehow to bring irritation and distress into situations which meant so much to you."

"We never played our game of snap."

Paul put the cards into his pocket.

"I gave you so little."

"You gave me all I needed."

Soon after my discharge from hospital, the rumours of a Russian withdrawal became a reality. One morning the departing tanks made the windows tremble. Later, marching soldiers in odd uniforms could be seen in the streets. The Lithuanian army had taken over Wilna. Now that the Russians had left the city, the Poles took revenge on the Jews. We did not know why. After all, the Jews had not profited from the Russian occupation. They were as poor now as they were before. Nobody had enough to eat. Most of the shops had remained closed. The old hatred, controlled only by the presence of a mighty army, flared up once more. Crowds of people massed themselves in the small lanes and alleys in the Jewish quarter, armed with sticks and clubs and iron bars, ready to beat up anyone who looked Jewish, trying to break open doors, smashing windows, setting alight houses. The Jews had locked themselves up, in their dingy rooms, in their shops protected by strong wooden shutters. Perhaps the population was angry about what had happened to them, angry about having been treated like pieces on somebody's chessboard, moved from here to there without being asked. The Jews were to blame. Somebody had to be blamed.

Paul and I stayed with the woman, the good woman in the café. We listened to the shindy outside in the street. Once it sounded as if the mob were able to rip open the barricades. We did not think of defending ourselves. Jews in Europe never thought there was a point in standing up for themselves.

"They will get us, whatever we do," the woman exclaimed.

But on this occasion they did not. There was a sudden stillness. The din in the streets had stopped. We heard what sounded like orders bellowed out and then further away the booming of heavy vehicles. Somebody knocked at the door and shouted something in Yiddish. The woman went to the door and carefully opened it.

The Russians had returned. The Russians were the friends of the Jews. They would look after the interests of the Jews. The Russians would protect us.

Jubilation. The Jews came out of their hiding places like ants from their nests in the ground. They sang. They danced. They praised the Lord.

Paul and I went back to the hostel. We had seen it all before, five years ago when the Nazis came. We did not feel we could dance in the street.

The Lithuanians must have assured the Russians that they would keep order. A day or two later, no Russian soldiers could be seen any more. Wilna had become Lithuanian. Wilna had become Vilnius. Lithuania was not at war. This meant that we could write to the parents. We could tell them we were safe. We decided to send them a telegram. We also wrote to grandfather who still lived, as far as we knew, in Breslau. I thought of writing to Georg and Toni, but somehow could not bring myself to do it.

We made some money. It was a unique opportunity. Each inhabitant was allowed to change fifty zloties — which had no value any more — into twenty-five Lits (the Lithuanian currency). Anyone would lend us zloties. We borrowed one hundred zloties — fifty for Paul and fifty for myself. All night we queued up outside the bank. The line of people was at least a mile long. We took it in turns to stand and wait, it was November and getting quite cold. We changed over every hour, one of us warming himself in the hostel while taking a rest. I had Paul's money when it was my turn at noon. I tried to explain to the clerk that I was also holding my brother's money — "he has fallen ill, Sir," — and was given fifty Lits. We could sell four Lits for one hundred zloties and returned the zloties to the lender. We had made forty-six Lits. We had made money out of nothing. A few days later Paul went on his own to try to get another twenty-five Lits. ("I have been ill and could not go to the bank the other day.") He obtained the money. We were rich.

We could go shopping. But there were still only a few shops open. We had the equivalent of several pounds in our pockets. What could we buy? We found a place which sold special biscuits. We became addicted to them. They were indeed very fine, sprinkled with sugar and cinnamon. And we bought halvah. I could sing a song of praise for halvah: this delicious confection, oblong, sticky, made of honey and sesame seeds.

"I'm not the only one who likes to eat good things," I said.

"These are extraordinary times. Eating has become very important," replied Paul, munching happily.

"I wonder when we shall hear from the parents," I said, "at least they know by now that we are safe."

We heard from someone who had managed to get to Wilna before the frontier between Lithuania and Russian-occupied Poland was closed, that Rudi, Ernst and Franz were safe in Bialystok, the town we wanted to reach originally.

"They did not go to Romania after all," I said.

"They must have changed their minds on the way."

"I wonder why they decided against coming here?"

"Rudi was a communist. Perhaps he persuaded the others that there would be better opportunities for them under Russian rule."

"Now we have no chance of thanking them. We shall never know how they found out that we were kept in a cell in Lubartow."

"If we had not been too worn out that night to change trains, perhaps we would be with them today," said Paul.

"And not have been able to get in contact with the parents."

"I know what you're thinking, Martin."

The airmail letter arrived during the next week. A letter from England. A letter from the parents. I tore it open. Tears welled up.

I found a quiet corner.

Here was mother's familiar handwriting.

It had not changed.

She wrote as she had always written, like a school-girl, filling out every space on the thin paper, right down to the bottom and then in all four margins. She had left only room for a brief message from father.

I read:

'We did not think we would ever hear from you again, my darlings, no, it was I who did not have any hope. Father believed you would write to us one day. Now that we know where you are, we shall move heaven and earth to get you here.

'We are still living in Richmond. Your father has been a great comfort to me, he really has had a lot to put up with, you can imagine what a state I was in. Father always said we would be together again, that the day would come when I would see you both again. Whether he really was so sure, I do not know. Our landlady here is psychic. She repeatedly told me that she had 'seen' you several times in the barren landscape. She told us she was certain you would get in touch with us, as soon as you had reached your goal. Oh, my dearest children, how relieved we are. I cannot put my feelings into words. Father made me do a lot of blackberry picking in Richmond Park. This helped me to take my mind off my fears. Write to us soon. Your ever loving mother.''

Father wrote:

'Very happy. Your cousin Bruno is already in touch with the Home Office. Mother and I are well. Do you need any money? Much love, your Dad.'

In spite of my still sore legs, I ran to the University library where Paul was reading. The joy of telling him we had had a letter from the parents was even greater than having the letter itself. Would his face show surprise, doubt, happiness? 'Paul,' I'll say, 'the times of despair are over.' I felt feverish, running through the street. Gasping for breath I climbed the stairs outside the library. There was the reading room. He sat by the window, where he always sat, still in his brown-checked coat, a small, fragile figure. I stood away from him, catching my breath and savouring the moment of anticipation. Now I walked towards him. He had seen me already. He looked at me and knew at once.

"We've heard?"

I passed the letter to him. He read it through, quickly, with a small smile. He raised his eyebrows and said quietly: "You always knew, Martin. You always knew."

Walking back to the hostel, everything seemed to have changed. Some snow had fallen. It was glittering in the hazy December sun. The streets looked wider, the squares more spacious. The trees carried narrow white bridges of snow. Even the spanning arches in the alleys and the wet iron railings proclaimed a certain importance. All was the same, yet everything had been transformed.

We walked arm in arm, talking, of course, about the parents. We had to make an effort and get closer to them. We should not expect them to understand us. It was not necessary for them to enter our thinking, our feelings, our very souls. It was preposterous to make such demands on them. They had drawn us towards them. They had waited for us, were still waiting. This waiting was significant, had meaning, was decisive. Why should they take an interest in my poetry? What had I done to make them believe in me as an artist? Had I shown that I wanted to share in their concerns, their anxieties? How often did I deprecate father's efforts? And complain about mother's lack of tact? Did I not withdraw from them on many occasions when I went on my solitary walks, even considered emigration without them, without paying regard to their feelings. All this would be different from now on. Paul said we must become more indulgent, more patient, less concerned with ourselves. I said that I had not loved them enough. Paul said that an understanding of the weakness of those you care about should not lead to rejection. I said that my longing for the parents must be a sign of a deeper attachment than I imagined. Paul said, that it was important to remember that the parents would be the same people as they had been six months ago when they left us. I said that one could not really know how particular experiences affected people. At least I hoped *I* was different from what I had been before the march through Poland.

As I did not want to join Paul who spent many hours in the

reading room, I attached myself to one or two of our room mates. There was Bamberg, lean, weatherbeaten, with a leathery wrinkled face. He had been a farmer in the Bohemian part of Czechoslovakia. As work on the land might be a possibility for some of us, either here in Lithuania or elsewhere, he gave lectures on the theory of farming.

I had, for some time, fancied myself as a farmer. Close to the soil. Married to nature. The books of the Norwegian writer Hamsun had impressed me when I was younger. Men and women living in the country, were they not closer to God than towns' people? Did they not witness, day be day, the rising of the sun? Did they not grow with the seasons? Could they not taste the wind with their tongues? They dug deep into the earth, they planted and observed growth. They looked skywards, knowingly. A farmer is more human and more humble. I was certain I would make a good farmer. There would also be time left to write poems and stories, especially in winter when the soil rested.

Bamberg's lectures showed — or so I thought — that he had no vision. Farming for him was just hard work, like carpentry. He talked about the tools, the planning of crops, the possible pitfalls in farming. Perhaps he is not a very good farmer, I thought. Surely farming was different from other occupations. It demanded more than knowledge and skills. Belief in the goodness of life was necessary, belief in the natural order, in short: belief in God.

I decided not to attend Bamberg's lectures any more.

Fortunately Herr Fink proposed another activity for me. Herr Fink, a burly man with very red cheeks, had been a singer with the Vienna Folk Opera. He had given a short recital in the Refugee Centre. Even Paul was impressed by his voice. He had admitted that he had sung small parts only and sometimes had taken over a major role at matinee performances.

"If Hitler had not come to Austria last year, maybe I could have made a name for myself," he said.

Herr Fink had heard me singing while I was busy cleaning the washroom.

"You have a good voice," he said to me, "excellent material. Needs to be trained and moulded, of course. What

250

about joining a new Jewish Opera Company, which is about to be formed? I can introduce you to the conductor. I'm sure he will be only too glad to give you an audition."

"Will you be a member of the Company?" I asked.

"Of course, my boy, of course. I shall sing Radames in 'Aida'. This was Slezak's role. Have you heard of Leo Slezak? Another Austrian tenor. Magnificent, my boy, magnificent. There is no other Radames like him. Mind, he's not singing any more, he's getting on, you know, but there is, after all, Walter Fink, ha ha, and I've had some lessons from Slezak anyway."

Paul said if I was accepted, it would be an interesting experience. He warned me that I could not expect to become a star overnight.

I impressed the musical director, a shy, dark young man, who agreed with Herr Fink, who had come with me to the audition, that my baritone voice (he called it 'second tenor') showed promise and should be developed. Rehearsals for *Aida* were going to start shortly. I would be very welcome to join the chorus. I was very pleased, perhaps just a little disappointed that I had not been cast for a small part.

*   *   *   *

An actor. As a child it had often been necessary to pretend to be someone else. I was not like other people. I hated seeing myself in the mirror. I wanted to be handsome, like the boys I knew. But this was not possible. At least I could try to impersonate others. In the street where I played, I stopped people and informed them that I was a policeman in plain clothes and that they were suspected of robbing a bank. Some pedestrians looked annoyed, others joined in the game. In my Junior School I once took the part of a 'gentleman'. (They painted a thick moustache above my lips.) It was a well-known joke. A 'lady' asked me to show her the way to an old aunt. My instructions on how to find the address were so long, complicated, rambling, wordy, spun-out, that finally the 'lady' decided not to listen any more. The audience, mothers, fathers, uncles and aunts, were in fits of laughter. They all enjoyed my antics thoroughly.

251

Somebody talked to my mother and seriously suggested that I should go on to the stage.

Paul always disliked my clownish behaviour. It was not that he lacked a sense of humour. But my efforts embarrassed him. I would suddenly, without reason, fall into clownery. I would talk nonsense or imitate the voices of well-known personalities. I would sing *Sonny Boy* like Al Jolson, or *You are my Heart's Delight* like Richard Tauber. Once or twice I managed to fool my mother. I would act like a very sick child and was allowed to stay away from school. There was an occasion when I told my parents and Paul that I had seen a motor car speeding along the main road to the South Park without a driver. I spoke with such conviction that I convinced myself and flew into a temper when it was suggested that I was not telling the truth. But when I rushed once into my parents' bedroom, hot and breathless, and announced that two white mice were hiding under the sideboard in the dining-room, was I lying? I still think I saw two white mice. My father did not often intervene. But this time he wanted to teach me a lesson. He took me by the hand, we walked together into the dining-room and looked under the sideboard.

"If you go on making up these stories," he said, "nobody will like you."

"But I did see white mice, I did, I did."

He drew with his forefinger a cross on my forehead.

"Everybody will see the cross. It is a warning not to believe you."

I hurried to my room and looked into the mirror.

There was no cross on my forehead. No cross.

Going into the passageway I met my mother.

"You have got a cross on your forehead," she said, "Martin, you must not lie."

Grandfather was in the entrance hall.

"Is there a cross on my forehead?"

"Oh yes. I can see it," grandfather said.

Paul saw it. The cook saw it. The maid saw it. But there was no cross. I could not see it.

This was real theatre. I still do not know how father had directed the play. For me reality and fantasy were not

252

two separate worlds. The small boy lived in both worlds simultaneously and often intensely. He could not always differentiate between what was true and what was not. When he was older he played such acting games silently. He had learnt by then that his buffoonery had to be kept to himself. The grown-ups did not appreciate it. On his solitary walks he imagined himself to be good looking, gifted, independent and respected by everybody. Perhaps an artist. An actor. A violinist. Applause rung in his ears. Standing near a lamp-post he bowed and smiled graciously. If an unexpected lone passer-by glanced at him and shook his head, the boy called out:

"It's all right. I'm not really mad. I am just rehearsing for a school play."

One day the Silesian Opera Company approached my Grammar School. They wanted some boys for their new production of Pfitzner's *Palestrina*. I was known to sing well. But I was not selected. The music master was very apologetic. He said that I was not suitable for the part. But I knew otherwise.

And it hurt.

* * * *

Now I was to become a member of an Opera Company. I knew that many a great singer had started in the chorus. After a while I would be given small parts to sing, then larger ones and finally I would be given a plum role. I would be famous.

Paul was forgotten, and the parents, and our situation. Everything had faded into the background. Once again I played a game. I knew, of course, that the opera project was not realistic. Herr Fink said that there were plans to take the Company to Palestine, and to the United States and perhaps even to Mexico.

"You wait and see," said Herr Fink, "we are both sitting on a winner, my boy."

I did not share his optimism.

And yet, I looked forward to being a member of the Company.

253

I went to the first rehearsal. I noticed that everyone in the chorus seemed to be able to sight read. I have always been good at imitating simultaneously, it was very much like a game I had played with Paul when the lights had been turned off. But this I could not keep up for long. I had to learn to sing what the notes dictated. Who was there to teach me?

There was deep snow. An icy wind was sweeping through the streets. We had been given one winter coat, which Paul and I shared. I went out with Blume in Paul's thin brown summer coat. Blume took me out of the town. The whiteness was blinding. We did not talk much to each other. Blume hardly ever talked. He was a strange man. Heaps of old newspapers tied with string were neatly stacked under his bed. Sometimes we saw him untying one of the parcels, apparently looking for a particular issue and smiling to himself when he had found it. Then he put the pages back with great care where they had been before. Nobody asked him why he collected old newspapers. Amongst the refugees there was an unspoken understanding that no one interfered with what individuals did.

Still, it was odd, this hoarding of newspapers, and it was Blume's oddness which attracted me to him. When he spoke, one could hardly hear him. He had a sister who lived in Birmingham, whom he loved very much. He hoped he would be together with her one day.

We walked silently in the silent snow. I remembered the snow in Breslau and I felt as I did when I was little: a feeling of intimacy, of nearness, of wholeness, as if the quietness around me had entered me and had taken possession of me.

My ears sang.

My throat hurt.

As soon as we were back at the hostel, I sank onto my bed. Paul was leaning over me. Then Blume, shaking his old face and touching with trembling fingers my flushed face.

I heard him saying to Paul: "He shouldn't have come with me."

I asked for water.

The doctor came and shone a torch into my mouth.

"Peritonsillar abscess," he told Paul and I did not know or care what this meant. I had a high fever. I had become ill at the wrong time. The hostel was going to move in a couple of days to new premises. We had been told that in comparison with our present quarters, the new place would seem like a luxury hotel. Paul and I had been wondering who was going to pay for the furnishing and the rent. There was some talk that an American Refugee Organisation would be funding the new hostel. The prospect was exciting. Paul told me later that the doctor had expressed some doubt as to whether I could move in my condition and he had advised admission to hospital. Paul had persuaded him that another separation from the group was likely to have a bad effect on me and that he would see to it that I was cared for adequately. They wrapped me up in several blankets and practically carried me down the stairs. I was very giddy. It was dark outside. The snow threw off its own light. The sledge was waiting. The horse was snorting and steaming. They bandaged me with rags. The mummy, Martin. Only my eyes could be seen. Paul sat next to me.

The dark, medieval city flew by. The city, like a bride in a festive dress. Whatever was ugly had now been covered up. Newness. Only my rapid heartbeat disturbed the stillness. Where was I riding to? To England. To England. Through the clouds across the white plains. Paul, are you there? Did I not tell you we would make it? They are waiting. We must hurry. Driver, don't whip the horse. Our Pegasus.

'Who is riding so late through the night and the wild? It is the brother with a child.' Hold me tight, Paul, hold me. If I must die, let me die now. Paul, love the parents for me.

*   *   *   *

It was good to be ill when I was a child. My mother looked after me, no one else was allowed to do so. My mother took me over. More than that. It was almost as if I could creep back into her. Once again I became hers. I was secure. She turned away from her friends, from her husband, from her older son. All appointments were cancelled. She sent out

255

the maid to do the shopping. She would devote herself entirely to me. When I was feverish the paediatrician would be telephoned at any time of the day or night. He came, examined me and then began to treat mother: reassure her and instruct her. Every four hours she was to take my temperature, sliding the vaselined thermometer into my backside, she had to give me the prescribed medicine regularly, and not to forget, of course, the cold water poultices. Oh, these poultices. In spite of my pleadings, all through the day she came to my bed with the wet, icy-cold cloth, wrapped it around my neck, on top of it the oily, evil-smelling yellow covering (to prevent the water from seeping through), and a long thick woollen stocking. I could hardly move my neck afterwards. How I hated those compresses. How I hated her coming to my bed, two safety-pins between her lips and the bits and pieces over her arm. I begged her to leave me for another hour or so, but she would not listen. How I loved her for caring for me.

Then she sat next to my bed and sang one of the sentimental songs her mother had sung to her when she was little:

"I have lost my steed,
    my beautiful steed . . . "

Mother would see to it that an egg was beaten up with lots of sugar and a little milk. When I was getting better I was given chicken broth and during convalescence I could choose what I ate. ("As long as the child eats, all is well.") When Paul came home from school and he had finished his homework, he would read to me. Grandfather would put his head around the door and show his concern and father hurried home earlier in the evening than usual.

I had become important.

My illnesses were the common childrens' ailments or feverish chills or attacks of tonsillitis, but once my persistent cough was not regarded as serious by my mother. Perhaps she thought (with some justification) that I wanted to avoid going to school. In the end she did take me to the doctor. He diagnosed pneumonia which had already passed its climax. My mother was beside herself. How could she let this happen? Her child suffering from pneumonia and she had not known.

She tortured me with her care.
But I wanted to be wanted.
Her physical ministrations met both our needs.

*   *   *   *

Our new hostel was a vast improvement on what we had been used to before. My bed was in the corner by the door in a room which I shared with Paul and two others. The mattress was filled with straw but I was lying on a soft white pillow. Coloured blankets covered me. Blume's bed was near the window, (he still blamed himself for my illness, mumbling and gesticulating,), and the bed of an elderly man who spent much time stuffing tobacco into thin paper tubes. He sold them to a source which he kept secret.

After a few delirious days, I did not mind being ill. The old sensations returned. True, mother was not here, but there was Paul, and the others came to my bedside from time to time and wished me well. I listened to the familiar humming in my ears, a sign of high temperature. When I was little I thought this was the sound the earth was making, turning round and round. I ran my fingers along the folds of the blankets on my chest, climbing hills, jumping across abysses, sliding down ravines. I lost myself in the complicated pattern of the wallpaper. I listened to the strange sounds in the house.

Paul read out a letter from grandfather: " 'My dear boys. It gave me very great pleasure to hear from you again. I am so relieved you survived the war in Poland and are safe now in Lithuania. When you are reunited with the parents, give them my love. I am still living with the same family, which takes good care of me, and I think often of the many years when we were all living together. Your loving grandfather.' " I could see that Paul was moved.

Paul told me that the Committee in Kaunas (the capital of Lithuania at that time) was trying to get British visas for some of us. Nobody seemed to know much about what was done to make this possible and the Committee members rarely came here to Wilna. The chairman was Herr Sonnental, a portly man with a face like a good uncle, always jovial and

257

perhaps a little ridiculous.

"The food here is excellent," said Paul, "I am sorry you have to make do with milk and soup at the moment. But your interest in food has not diminished, I expect. You have got something to look forward to. Pestel is the cook. He comes from Hungary. Hungarian goulash. Czech potato noodles. Austrian dumplings. Where he gets the ingredients from, nobody knows. The portions are not very big, but one learns again to appreciate good cooking."

"Strange words coming from your lips," I said.

My fever abated suddenly. Still in bed, I was plagued one afternoon by one of those childhood attacks which had frightened me so much when I was little. Here it was again. It is not easy to describe it. Vision, touch and hearing became distorted. Objects grew larger and moved towards me or became smaller and withdrew into the distance. The texture of the sheet or blanket became smoother or rougher and the slightest sounds changed into roaring noises. Even a mere whisper was like a shout and I begged the people who stood around the bed helplessly to be very quiet. In the past, the only one who could drive away these spirits (as a child I thought I was visited by them) was mother. When she put her hand on my forehead, I would soon be freed from these vexing sensations. But now there was only Paul and some friends witnessing my distress. Their faces grew enormously, their arms hung from their shoulders like thick cobras and their fingers resembled large animal tentacles.

Then, all of a sudden, everything was normal once again.

After a few more days, I got up and haltingly shuffled to the window. There was still snow in the streets and long fantastically shaped icicles hung from the gutters. People clad in furs, with thick scarves wound round their necks, went to and fro, as if they knew where they were going. Paul came into the room and, seeing me by the window scolded me:

"Get away from the window, Martin. It's much too cold over there."

I turned round, facing him.

"I was so worried about you," he said quietly.

It was good to be well again.

Life in the hostel was pleasant, not only because of the good cooking. It did not take us long to learn to live in this civilised setting, as if we had never been divorced from it.

I did not want to take part in the opera rehearsals any more. Herr Fink felt let down. I did not feel like going out, it was warm and friendly in the hostel. But one Saturday after breakfast I was asked whether I should like to go to a nearby synagogue. I was not very keen, but as there was nothing else to do — Paul was upstairs in the flat of Pestel's girlfriend, playing the piano — I told Chaim Bernstein that I would go with him. I knew Chaim only slightly — he had arrived in Wilna rather later than most of us — and wondered why he had invited me. He had caught me out once, when I was observing him making the elaborate preparations before intoning his morning prayers. He was an orthodox Jew and wore, during his prayers, his tallith, the fringed prayer-shawl, but fuller and longer than I had ever seen. He also put on the tefillin, the two lengthy strips of leather with small leather boxes. These contain writings from the old testament on tiny pieces of parchment. The phylacteries are to remind Jews to keep the law. Chaim explained this to me later. Chaim took a long time placing the tefillin near his heart, coiling one strap seven times around his left forearm, putting the other little box in the centre of his forehead, high up where hair normally grows (but he was quite bald). Then the strap was twisted round his head and he made a knot. The ends he brought backwards and forwards and the front bit of one strap he wound three times round his wrist and knuckles. It was all so complicated.

I could not make it out.

'So pointless, all this,' I thought. 'Are such rituals really essential?' Chaim had done all this slowly and deliberately, unconcerned with the goings-on in the room. I wondered whether the roof crashing down would disturb him. He saw me watching him, but he only spoke to me after the prayers.

"You have never seen a Jew praying, Martin?" There was no hint of sarcasm.

"In a synagogue, yes. But not on his own. No, not like

this."

"Well, now you have."

"Why are all these rituals so important to you?"

"They make you feel like a Jew. You go to services on Sabbath?"

"Not any more. I used to go on New Year and Atonement days. We always had tickets then. Sometimes I went on Saturdays."

"You talk about the past."

"Well, I have not been for years."

"Why not? Why did you stop going?"

"My parents were not orthodox. In the liberal synagogue in Breslau, we had a cantor who was once an opera singer, I was told. People went to the synagogue mainly to hear him sing. He did sing beautifully. Even when I was a boy, I liked to listen to him."

"Well?"

"There was something about the service which I found repelling, objectionable, no, these words are too strong, off-putting. Yes, it was like going to a concert. You bought your tickets for the High Festivals, you had your allocated seats, you listened to the wonderful singing and you were annoyed when the second cantor with the squeaky voice, for some reason had taken over. And at the end of the service, the families assembled in the courtyard and talked about the music and the singing. I did not like that. It was best when I was not well enough to go to the synagogue and I could stay at home."

"At home? What did you do when you were on your own?"

"I sat by the window and looked into the night sky. Gazing at the stars and the ever-moving moon, I felt close to God."

"And you prayed?"

"Yes, I prayed. Soundless prayers. Of course, I did not refuse to go to the synagogue. My parents would not have understood."

"There is a place for praying by yourself and a place for praying as a member of the congregation. But you stopped attending services?"

260

"When we lived in Brünn I went once with mother on a Friday evening. There was a magnificent choir. I knew then that I would not go any more. As I was already seventeen, my parents did not insist."

"And you have never been to an orthodox service?"

"It would not mean much to me. I only learnt sufficient Hebrew for my Bar Mitzvah."

Now I was going with Chaim to the synagogue.

"Sabbath is the holiest of holy days," he said, "I don't even wear tefillin on Saturdays."

"Why not?"

"Jews are not permitted to do so. Sabbath is holy enough without them."

It was not really a synagogue, as I knew it. 'Shul' was a prayer room in one of the narrow, smelly lanes, not far from the café where Paul and I had sat on so many occasions. The room was sparsely furnished. Some old wooden benches for the congregation. The Holy Ark which contained the scrolls resembled an antique wardrobe. There was a flat table covered with a green cloth in front of the Ark. We were perhaps two dozen men, everyone except me wearing the wide silken shawl. There were no women. I looked up: no gallery, where the women usually sat separated from the men. There was no organ. No choir. The service was simple, entirely in Hebrew. I tried to follow it in the prayer book which Bernstein had given me. I soon had to give up. I knew too little of Hebrew. Bending, swaying and rocking, each man belonged to himself and to his neighbours. Yet, they were all linked together. Only I was the outsider. Here I could not pray. The chanting happened outside me. Their dialogue with God could not be shared by me. I had no part in it. The Ark was opened and two scrolls were lifted out. This was something I was familiar with. The scrolls looked like dressed-up infants. One was placed on the shoulders of the rabbi. Another man carried the smaller one of the two. They both walked singing through the small congregation. Each man bowed as they passed him. And returning, the two nannies sat down and two other men undressed the infants. The crowns and the ringing and pinging fineries were taken off. Then the outer garments. Then the cloth

261

next to the bodies. Then the umbilical cord which holds the scroll together was untied. Nakedness. The naked scrolls were lifted up and shown to the congregation. Bare wisdom, They did not need adornment. And yet, I felt as I had always felt, ill at ease. Even at my Bar Mitzvah when the scroll, unrolled, was placed on the table for me to read the carefully prepared passage, I could not help thinking that this stripped babe was likely to catch cold.

*   *   *   *

My Bar Mitzvah had been delayed. This important ceremony, signifying the newly acquired status of adulthood, should have been celebrated nearer my thirteenth birthday, but it took place when I was fourteen. It was a simple affair. Unlike Paul's. That had been a splendid occasion. After the service in the synagogue, there had been a reception in our flat. Scores of people came. Scores of presents. Literary works, bound in leather. Suitcases in different sizes. Useless manicure sets (why would boys need a manicure set?). Watches, alarm clocks, several pairs of expensive cuff-links and tie-pins, several fountain pens, silver and gold propelling pencils. There was too much of everything. But of course I, nine years old, thought how marvellous it must be to get all these presents.

"It will be the same when you have your Bar Mitzvah," my father said.

In the evening there was a dinner at the hotel 'Four Seasons', (the same hotel where Hitler stayed several times some years later). Paul had to make a speech which he had written himself. I can still see his pale, strained face. His voice was trembling. He thanked the parents, grandfather, the Rabbi (who was a guest of honour), the relatives (all those uncles and aunts who had never taken much interest in us, with the exception of one or two), his friends and acquaintances. He thanked them all for having helped him towards maturity, for making the day so memorable, for being there. According to custom, I sat with the other children at a table specially set aside for us. It occurred to me, listening to my older brother, that he had not thanked me. After all, I had given him a present (bought and paid for by the parents). We had played together. Paul should have thanked me too.

I comforted myself: 'You just wait until I have my Bar Mitzvah. Then they will all come and make a fuss of me.'

But times had changed. The year was 1934. The Nazis had already been in power for a year. A reception, more modest than on the previous occasion, was arranged. As it was unwise to have dinner at the hotel, it was to take place in our own home. I was not really disappointed when I was told. Presumably presents would still be given. There was a row about who should and who should not be invited to dinner. After all, space was very limited. In the end the parents decided to cancel the dinner altogether. I did not mind. It meant that I did not have to prepare a speech. It was a quiet reception. People I knew well, and some I did not know at all, came, put on a smile, shook hands with me, had a glass of wine and a bridge roll, and went away again. The two presents which gave me most pleasure were the beautiful bicycle (from my parents) and a book meant for younger children by Erich Kästner. I was fourteen, but not yet mature. In the evening, the parents, grandfather, Paul and I went to a restaurant where Jews were still welcome. For several months I had attended lessons in Hebrew to prepare me for the occasion, together with Toni who, to my great joy, was going to have his Bar Mitzvah on the same day. There was another boy whom I knew from school, who was supposed to be the third to join us, but he told his parents that he was not going to submit himself to the indignity of an outdated ritual. It was against his own belief, a belief in the non-existence of God. When he told Toni and me about the frightful arguments he had had with his parents, we were both shocked.

"You must have hurt your parents," said Toni.

"It's no good pretending. It's better to come clean. My parents already knew that I was an atheist."

"So you told them that you did not wish to go through with it?" I asked.

"I did. Why should I conform, merely to please my folks?"

It seemed incredible that he took such a stand. Against his parents. What did it mean anyway, to be an atheist? I was ignorant. Here was a school mate I had known for several years. He did not seem to be so different from the rest of us. This boy, who held a belief different to that of his parents, who had made up his mind independently, who was not willing to do what his parents expected him to do, who was prepared to fight for it, stepped out, tore himself away, made a decision. And here was I, always doing as I was told, never questioning the parents, acting according to their wishes, having no strong convictions which I thought I should defend if necessary. Any kind of rebellion was unthinkable. I was an extension of my parents, outwardly at least. My 'inner life' was only shared with Georg or Paul, my parents knew nothing about it, and did not wish to know. How I admired that boy. What courage. How small I felt. How feeble I was.

But he had his Bar Mitzvah the following year. I spoke to him soon afterwards.

"I broke under the pressure," he said, "in the end I said, yes, yes. My father told me that I did not have to believe. 'Do it for the sake of your parents,' my father said. I was too tired to resist any more."

'We are not so different after all,' I thought.

But the service on the day of my Bar Mitzvah had meant something to me. We all walked to the tram-stop. The young leaves on the trees bordering the avenue were illuminated by the spring sun. I imagined that every person we saw on the way must know where we were going. My personal relationship with God could now be made public. My affirmation was going to be made in front of witnesses. Anyhow, I was going to perform. Paul said to me later, that I had read the extracts from the torah (the five books of Moses) with the skill and expression of somebody who had studied the Pentateuch all his life. I had also been chosen by ballot to read the Haftorah, a chapter from the Prophets. (Toni was a good loser.) I had performed well, I the actor, as I had intended. The synagogue had been a splendid theatre in its vastness. In my mind, I saw the curtain rise in front of me. The congregation, the audience, watched me, young, talented, full of promise. It was a great experience.

When I was on my own, late that night and nearly asleep, I asked for God's forgiveness. "This is how I am," I whispered into the pillows, "I like to play. But I did feel you inside me."

It was the end of January and very cold. We spent the days in gentle order. We corresponded with the parents. They had sent us some money. We continued buying the special biscuits and halvah. We knew now for certain, that the Committee in Kaunas was trying to arrange transport for those people who had relatives living in England. Herr Sonnental, the chairman, on his last visit here, had taken Paul and me to an empty room.

"Now you brothers Rosen," he had said. "You are on the list. You will see your parents soon. But don't say anything to the others. And by the way, I hear you have got to share a winter coat. That won't do, won't do at all. You can't travel to London with one coat, can you? We shall arrange something. You will hear from me."

We didn't really believe the news about the impending journey. The last letter from the parents had been full of hope, true, but father was always inclined to be over optimistic. During my convalescence a photographer had come and had taken our pictures. These were necessary, we had been told, for certain applications which had to be made on our behalf. But England was at war. Why should they bother about a few destitute refugees?

"They did not bother six months ago. Why give us permits now? Surely they have more important things to do?" Paul said.

I agreed with him but did not say so.

A week later we got the message that either Paul or I should travel to Kaunas to collect a winter coat. We wondered why the coat was not sent to us. Kaunas was more than one hundred kilometres away from Wilna.

We did not want to be awkward. There were others who made the decisions. Members of the Committee lived apart from us. Herr Sonnental was an important man. One must not get on the wrong side of him. We did not know much about the others, the elite, the refugee aristocracy. It was the committee which was in charge of funds, pulled the necessary strings and was, so we were told, in touch with other countries, Palestine, the USA and countries in South America.

m

Herr Sonnental had said that we would soon be with the parents. He did not say 'perhaps' or 'may be'. He was certain. Perhaps Paul's pessimism was not justified. There must be something in it. But it seemed so unlikely that Great Britain would give us visas. Still, there was no need for Herr Sonnental to say anything at all. He could have kept quiet.

Now one of us had to go to Kaunas to collect a coat. There was some secrecy about the whole operation. The less people knew the better. It was I who went to Kaunas. Like a school excursion. Going without mother's permission. Nobody was supposed to know. The others might jump to conclusions. Hopes could be raised unnecessarily. When I returned in the evening I was just going to say that I'd got a new coat without explaining how and where from.

Sitting in the train, I felt uncomfortable. Was I doing something wrong? Not because of the coat, of course. Nobody could blame me for getting a new coat. But travelling to Kaunas without anybody knowing about it. Linking the coat with getting to England, knowing that not everyone would get a visa, aware that Paul and I had been selected, picked out from a large number of people who had become our friends, there was something underhanded about it, as if we were involved in some crooked deal.

I was quite looking forward to walking around a new town on my own, but during the journey I became frightened.

Here I was, in a compartment with strangers, on my way to a strange place and Paul was already many miles away. I felt excluded and alone, and being separated from him was painful. Sudden stabs in my chest. We had managed with one coat so far, not much of the winter was left, why had I agreed to go and fetch a coat? What if something happened which would prevent me from returning? So much had happened without any warning during the last six months. What about that man, sitting opposite me, who is he? Does he know perhaps, what sort of traveller I am? He might get up and face me and threaten me and shout: "Get up and get out. Jump off the train, you foreigner, you German Jew, we don't want you here, get off and walk. Go anywhere, away from us. We don't want you. You hear, we don't want you."

And all would begin again: the despair, the horror. Only

Paul would not be with me. 'He'll be safe,' I thought, 'I'll manage somehow. I'll make my way back to him. Paul will not suffer, he'll not fall ill again. He's in a warm room. He won't be hungry. Whatever happens to me is not so important. I shall be able to bear it. I know I shall, not because I am stronger than Paul, but because I shall be led.'

I spotted Herr Sonnental on the platform. He held a large parcel. I walked over to him and took the coat, wrapped in strong brown paper.

"You can't go to your parents without it," Herr Sonnental said, "and I must tell you, that I hope to be able to give you good news in a few weeks."

We were walking towards the barrier. Herr Sonnental had become silent. Only when we were in the street, he almost pushed his head into my face and whispered:

"We still have to overcome some difficulty about passports."

I spoke loudly: "But we have got our German ones." I was excited.

"Hush. Don't speak so loud. You can't use your German passports."

I looked puzzled.

"Don't ask me any questions. Over there is a restaurant. I shall come inside with you and order something for you. Then I must go. Remember me to your brother."

I was served a large terrine with soup and pieces of boiled meat. The people around me spoke a very odd-sounding language. As soon as I had finished I hugged the parcel and left. I knew what I was going to do. I did not want to explore the town. I wanted to get back to the hostel. I wanted to be with Paul and tell him what Herr Sonnental had told me. Relieved, I entered the station. The train back to Wilna was just pulling in.

"You've missed something," said Paul. He found it difficult to suppress a smile.

"The Landowskis," he continued, "as usual they were at it after lunch. Ringel kicked up a shindy."

'At it,' meant that they had made love and Ringel was

known to be a sourpuss. He was elderly and full of bitterness. He had complained often enough that he was forced to live in a place which resembled a brothel. The Landowskis were a young couple, very much in love with each other. They had got married just shortly before the outbreak of war. She was small, dumpy and giggly. He was short and plump with an intelligent expression. He wore thick glasses. The couple did not conceal from us that they needed each other. They shared a room with Ringel and another woman. They had pushed their beds together to make a double bed in a corner of the room which was next to ours. The corner was screened off with a large green blanket hanging from a line. Soon after lunch they always left. Everybody knew they were going to bed to enjoy each other. However, on this occasion Ringel complained of a headache, he wanted to lie down. When he went upstairs and opened the door to the room, he could not help overhearing what was going on in the corner. He was furious when he returned to the dining-room. But he must have known like the rest of us, that the tactful thing to do was to keep out. Everybody was talking, stimulated by the incident, about love, tolerance, society, hang-ups, Ringel (who had rushed out of the house), the Landowskis (who had not yet come downstairs) and life in the hostel which should not debar people from having fun in bed.

During my illness I had not become aware immediately of what was happening next door. Still suffering from fever, I was puzzled. Unfamiliar noises. Did I imagine them? The creaking of the bedsprings, the man's pleading, the woman's exclamations, the laughter, the sighing, the shrieks and then the silence which was almost frightening in its completeness. When I knew what it meant I became excited myself. I thought of my own fleeting encounters. What it must be to make a relationship with a woman in the knowledge that there will be a next time and a next and a next, to be with her, to part and find her again, to grow with her. Would I ever find someone who wanted to be with me, day and night, accepting and loving? With me, the unattractive young man, burdened by the past, fearful of the future? And was I seriously prepared to commit myself? Had I ever shown that I could love without expecting something in return? Some response? So many — Paul for one — fell in love, demanding nothing, counting on nothing. The very glow of love was enough for them. To look at the girl, to talk to her, to be allowed to be with her, that was enough for Paul. Enough, in the constant hope that one day, one day perhaps she would turn to him, would want to be embraced by him, would be willing to embrace. But I stand on the edge, not moving forward, not even admitting that I am moved, waiting for a 'yes' without making the slightest effort to find out. Am I so frightened that I withdraw before even a beginning has been made? Is it that I fear rejection? Rejection because of my oddness, because of the way I speak, because of the way I am?

Years ago, when I was walking through the South Park with Georg, I told him, who knew nothing, what I knew of sex (knowledge gathered mainly from our ancient encyclopaedia at home). We talked then for hours about the need for fulfilment. We were certain that physical union could not be achieved without spiritual union. (But we could not define what we meant by physical union.) Two bodies, we agreed, could only fit together when two minds were fused. Grand thoughts. How long will I have to wait for this? And was it nothing to be with the young woman in Brünn on one single occasion? She had loved me, me whom she did not know, and I had loved her for loving me. Did this account for nothing? That beautiful act had been, I was sure, more than a passing physical thrill. But there is nobody now. I am alone. There is no one else but myself. Sounds could be heard from the room next door. I touched my eyes and let my fingers wander along the sides of my nose, my cheeks, my lower lip. I imagined myself caressed. Or was it that I was in love with myself?

There had been rumours for some days that the departure of a group of people was imminent. Paul was still incredulous and Martin tried to control his excitement.

One morning, at the beginning of March, Martin was told that the group would leave the following day. There was to be a meeting later, Herr Sonnental was expected.

Paul was not in the hostel, he was having his hair cut by the friendly barber in the shop where some months ago some valueless money had been collected for the brothers. Martin ran to the shop, talking loudly to himself.

"We're going. We're really going. Paul won't believe it. He'll think I am joking. But I'm not. Of course I'm not. We are going."

Martin was propelled forward. On and on. The people in the streets did not exist for him. There was only one thought: to tell Paul the news. Paul got out of the barber's chair when Martin entered the shop.

"Tomorrow," said Martin, trying to catch his breath, "tomorrow."

As they walked slowly back to the hostel, Martin said: "Sonnental will give us all the necessary information this afternoon."

"It's time for biscuits and halvah," said Paul, and they went and bought enough to take with them on the journey.

"I expect we shall have to join the army in England," said Paul.

"Probably."

"We tried before, but without success."

"Well this time it's going to be different."

"The war might last a very long time."

"Do you think so? Some people say it will be over soon."

"It doesn't look like it."

"There doesn't seem to be any fighting."

"It all depends when the British and the French take the initiative."

"Paul, this means nothing to me at the moment."

"What do you mean?"

"We're going to be with the parents, Paul."

"Yes, Martin. And don't eat all the biscuits now. Keep some for tomorrow."

There was agitation in the hostel.

Pestel, who was not on the list of those to leave, showed his disappointment:

"Who are these people who make up this so-called

270

committee? I bet they got themselves on the list. No doubt about that. Twenty altogether, only twenty. We are thirty-five here and another twenty-two in Kaunas. Only twenty got visas."

"Those with relatives in England," somebody said.

"That's what they say. I don't believe it."

"We shall be next, according to Sonnental."

"Don't kid yourself. We are going to stay behind and rot. Sonnental, the captain, is leaving the sinking ship. The whole thing stinks. Refugee money, our money, you hear, was given to certain officials to allow a small number of people to leave. A rotten deal to get a few of us to England. At the cost of the rest of us."

"You're upset. You don't know what you're talking about."

"I know, believe me, I know. I got the information from someone in the passport office. I've got a good mind to let the Lithuanian Police know. Then this business can be stopped."

Martin could not understand why Pestel, the always good-humoured and even jolly Pestel, was now making these threatening pronouncements. He really might cause trouble, stop them from going.

"It's not surprising what unhappy people are capable of doing," said Paul.

"Do you think that Pestel might denounce us?" asked Martin.

"It is best to be prepared for anything," replied Paul.

Herr Sonnental gave each a new passport. Martin opened his, and looked at a picture of a grave young man staring at him.

'This was taken when I was ill,' he thought, 'ill and full of doubts.'

The passports were not, in fact, passports, but 'Sauf-Conduits', as was explained at the top of the sheet in Lithuanian and French. Martin tried to remember the little French he had learnt in school. Profession: menuisier (stalius in Lithuanian). Blume, who was in the group, translated, "menuisier means carpenter."

Martin laughed out aloud, "Carpenter, and I can't even

271

hammer a nail straight."

Paul admitted that he had to write something down on the form. "Carpentry was the last thing you did, Martin."

Martin read, "Nationality: indeterminee. No, we haven't got a nationality, have we? Visage: oblong, couleur des yeux: bleue, signes particuliers — what does this mean?"

"Distinguishing marks," said Blume.

"Well, it's not filled in," said Martin and he was pleased.

Herr Sonnental explained that there had been some difficulty getting exit visas. The Germans had put pressure on the Lithuanian government not to let out refugees intending to cross the Baltic by boat or by plane. The Germans feared that refugees might go to Britain and join the army there. Hence the undetermined nationality in our passports. We were going to Riga, the capital of Latvia, via Kaunas, where we would pick up the others. In Riga we were to stay at a hotel overnight and take the plane — a Lufthansa plane, but there was nothing to worry about — to Stockholm. From there, via Oslo to Bergen and then, by boat to Newcastle.

"You'll get more details when we're on our way. It may take us some time to get to England. We shall sail in convoy and as yet we have no date. Anyone want to ask something?"

Blume wanted to ask Sonnental something. He had difficulty in spluttering out the words, "Pestel thinks . . ."

Sonnental interrupted him.

"I don't think we should take any notice of what Pestel says. It was difficult enough, believe me, to get the necessary papers and to obtain the exit visas. We had to use all our wits to outwit the Germans. We managed it. We are going."

"And the others?" somebody asked, "what are their chances of getting to England?"

"We shall leave no stone unturned, believe me, once we are in London. At present the British do not want to consider anyone unless he has got relatives waiting for him. That is the position. But we shall try and make them change their minds."

Paul spoke, "How secret is our trip?"

"It is not secret in the sense that it is not illegal. The Sauf-Conduits are legal documents and if you look at the entries of the visas they are quite genuine. But I would advise everybody not to draw attention to himself, not to speak loudly in German, particularly in Riga where the plane, a plane specially chartered for us, is waiting to take us to Sweden tomorrow. The Germans, if there are any Germans about, must be kept in ignorance of who we are, otherwise there could be complications. Latvia is a neutral country, and you might come across some Germans there. The best thing is not to talk at all when you see them."

"And if the Germans should stop us from leaving?"

"Look here," Sonnental was getting visibly annoyed, "we have been working on this project for months, believe me, many months. We have done everything humanly possible to arrange a safe journey to England. It costs a lot of money I'm telling you."

'And who is paying for this?' Paul wondered and he pressed his lips together and pushed his chin forward and shook his head. "May it end well," he mumbled.

Early next morning, people shook hands and embraced each other.

"We shall see that you join us as soon as possible," somebody said.

Pestel, quietened down, said in a cold menacing voice: "We shall see you back here tonight. You won't get far."

"Why, what have you done?" asked Martin, alarmed.

"Of course, he hasn't done anything," someone answered for him.

And then they walked out of the house, in silence.

In Riga they booked in at a large hotel. Two well-dressed men were talking to each other in German. They stood by the reception desk and looked at the new arrivals. The brothers went to their room, expecting a knock on the door at any moment.

"Do you think they know?" asked Martin, and he knew what a stupid question this was. How was Paul to know?

"Of course they know. The question is, whether they intend doing anything about it. Like us, they are in a foreign country."

Next morning the group was collected in a coach. On the way to the airport the coach broke down. An hour of anxious waiting, while the necessary repairs were carried out.

'It's strange that the coach should break down,' thought Martin.

In the airport they were hustled through the barrier. The plane was due to take off any minute. The official hardly looked at their Sauf-Conduits. Members of the crew spoke German to each other.

"Are they Germans?" Martin asked Paul, but Paul did not reply. They did not speak to each other until they were strapped into their seats.

"The pilot is certainly a German," said Paul, "this is a German plane, after all. Perhaps we are not flying to Stockholm."

"What do you mean?"

The plane was in the air. Martin looked anxiously at Paul.

"Königsberg is not far from here."

"You think we are being flown to Germany?"

"I don't know, of course, nobody knows. But the break-down of the coach, and the way they urged us on in the air-port, and then the pilot who looks as if he could be from the SS, are these mere coincidences?"

"You could be wrong, Paul."

"Of course, Martin. Nevertheless, we should prepare ourselves for the worst. I have had my doubts about the arrangements, anyhow. Herr Sonnental was very vague yesterday."

There was nothing to be seen outside, thick clouds obstructed the view. Martin wondered how they would fare in a concentration camp.

Then, suddenly, the sun broke through the clouds.

The brothers looked down on the roofs of large hangars.

There was writing on the roofs.

Large letters. Foreign words.

The plane was landing at the Stockholm airport.

From the moment I knew we were about to leave Wilna, I

lived in a kind of fever which turned everything around me into something which was not quite solid. I could not quite comprehend what was going on. Even the fear which once again had crept into me, was the fear of a dreamer. Pestel's outbursts and Herr Sonnental's confusing information were a kind of test for Paul and me. I can see that now. A test we failed. As in our darkest days in Poland, we were willing to surrender at the slightest hint of calamity. But there was a difference. The tempo had changed. I felt that now I was driven, pushed forward towards a destination already determined.

It was not, any more, a question of faith. I had lost contact with my personal God. Neither was it a matter which I could, or could not, accept. I was afraid, probably more afraid than Paul. I knew that wherever the plane might take us, that would be the goal, Königsberg or Stockholm or death in the Baltic. This knowledge, that an end was in sight, that a decision had already been made, that no effort of mine was needed, that I could let go, without having to resist, like an object moved on and on, did give me some comfort, and Paul's worries did not cut into me. And yet I was afraid. But this fear seemed to belong to someone else who observed us and took notice of our behaviour in this situation. I continued to fall in with Paul's anxiety, it had become a habit. I could do nothing else. I could not say to him: you are trying to destroy us both with your pessimism. Perhaps I should have said something to him. Perhaps I should have ordered him to keep his dark thoughts to himself. I did not. I failed. We both failed. Or I could have consoled him. I could have said: Have a little faith, Paul. Everything will work out, you wait. But I did not, although I was aware that this film was coming to an end and would not be rewound and repeated.

Perhaps I clung to Paul with such tenacity, because I already sensed that soon the time would come when we must unclasp our hands, when we must go our own ways, when the twin body would be transformed again into two separate bodies.

Our conversation after I had brought him the news of our imminent departure did wound me. Why did he talk about having to join the army? He must have known that he was

275

hurting me. Why do we always have to hurt each other so much?

How much do I care for other people? What about the people we had left behind: Fink and Bernstein and Bamberg and the Landowskis and Pestel, poor Pestel. Once we had left the building they had already faded into the background, they and all the others would soon disappear altogether.

(None of them was likely to have survived the war. No transport could be arranged for them to come to England.)

Cooks Travel had made the arrangements. Our group was taken from the airport by coach, to a very smart private hotel. The first 'help-yourself' meal was extravagant by any standard. On the long table dozens of dishes had been displayed: varieties of fish, meats, salads, cheeses, sweets, pastries, breads and biscuits. At first we were just speechless. It seemed incredible after Wilna, where there was so little choice of what to eat. Here you lived in order to eat, in Wilna you ate in order to live. And Wilna was only a few hours away by plane. We looked at the panorama of food in front of us, then discretion was thrown to the wind. Within half an hour there was little left. We had participated in an orgy of eating. Breakfast next morning was no different, but then we were asked to move out. This was not what the proprietor had bargained for. He was not prepared to feed twenty hungry refugees. We booked in at a hotel near the station. A separate dining-room was made available for the group, to avoid embarrassing the other guests. Food was a little more modest here but the style of living, altered so suddenly after our impoverished existence for so many months, the room with bath and telephone, the porters, lift boys and waiters, the well-dressed bejewelled guests we came across in the lobby and corridors: all this made us restless. Obviously we did not belong here. But we stayed in the hotel for a whole week waiting for further directions.

Stockholm was fairyland. It was as if the streets were laid with carpets. Nothing seemed to be old, even the Royal Palace looked youthful. And the luxurious stores, showing off thousands of goods, made us forget that it was war time. (Sweden was, of course, a neutral country.) The people in the street scrutinised us, in our bedraggled outfits with our haggard faces and staring eyes.

War was some kind of tragedy which happened somewhere else. Only the fighting between the Russians and the Finns was reported in the newspapers. But nobody was very concerned, although the battle took place not so far away from Stockholm, in the deepest snow. Anyway, a peace pact was expected to be signed shortly.

We walked through the streets of this gay, unaffected, relaxed city. We were strangers indeed. Was there not almost something obscene about the cheerfulness around us?

Father sent a telegram, giving us the address of an acquaintance of Bruno, our cousin. If we went to see him, we would be given some money to spend as we wished. He was an architect, living in a flat which he had designed for himself. Its modernity, the stainless steel furniture, the multi-coloured cushions, could not hide the unhappy man who lived in all this splendour. He was very disturbed about Sweden's neutrality and said that he loathed himself for colluding in the pretence that all was well with the world.

I let Paul decide how to spend the money we had been given. We went several times to the cinema and three times to performances at the Royal Opera House. (Mozart's *Cosi fan Tutti*, conducted by Fritz Busch, Verdi's *Traviata* and Leoncavallo's *Pagliacci* together with a one-act ballet.) Blume wanted to go to the circus and we agreed to go with him. As it happened, the star attractions were the 'Revels', the acrobatic clowns whom I had watched on my last day in Breslau, when I went with the parents and grandfather to the variety show. I had seen them at the beginning of our pilgrimage, with their funny antics on the trapeze. Were they now concluding it? After the performance Paul suggested we go somewhere to have some coffee. We spotted what looked like a modest little restaurant. The frontage of the place deceived us. A uniformed concierge welcomed us. He was extremely polite, but no doubt took notice of our threadbare clothes.

"Come with me," he said, leading us through a palatial hall. Ladies and gentlemen sat at small tables under palm trees, drinking from long glasses. They glanced at us, smiled benevolently and looked away quickly. Some showed annoyance. We followed the concierge. Did he intend to humiliate *us* or the wealthy guests? I felt like a condemned man walking through the abusing mob.

Finally we had reached the end of the long lounge. We stood in a small vestibule. The concierge opened the back door. Wind was blowing into our faces. He pointed vaguely somewhere in the distance and spoke in perfect German.

"Down the road you will find a café. Thank you, gentlemen."

The week flew past. One morning Sonnental told us that we would travel to Oslo that evening. Tomorrow, after breakfast, we would go on one of Europe's most famous and beautiful train journeys, to Bergen, the seaport.

He was right. Deep forests covered in glowing snow. Iced-up lakes, glaciers, steep mountains, abysses and rifts, crevices, long views into the distant wintry landscape. It was all too much, too much. At first nature seemed to speak to me as if to apologise for having stood apart in the days of agony. The tree, the hill, the frozen-up waterfall, the cliff: nothing has changed, nothing, it is still here for you to love, a voice was singing, it has been created for you. But I knew this was not so. I had been betrayed. What I had once loved so much, was outside, outside the window of the compartment, rushing by and away from me. When the train halted, it often stood in front of a large shed or snow screen, nothing could be seen then. But I did not really want to see. There was the memory of the dust in a bare landscape which had parched my throat. The pain of the heat, or the night sky lit up by flames. Nature had given me nothing then, no respite, no comfort. And now in its cold, fleeting display, it failed to woo me. It was only tiring. I was weary. Tunnels. More and more tunnels. I looked through a gap into some icy jewels, removed, detached. Everything was so far away. Nothing could be touched. Finally I let it all go by. It was already afternoon and getting dark. The tunnels were falling on top of each other. In the end there was more darkness than light. No, I thought, I am drained now. I have nothing to give. I shall not write poems any more. Let me be. Like

278

Paul and the others I had fallen asleep, while beauty danced wildly somewhere else.

As the brothers got ready for bed in the 'Hotel Rosenkrantz' in Bergen, they quarrelled. Neither could remember later what about. They fell asleep without having said good-night to each other.

In the morning when it was still dark, Martin got dressed and wrote a letter to Paul, an angry, bitter letter which was meant to hurt. Then he left the hotel. There was the bustle in the fish market. He was repulsed by the convulsing, silvery mass in the baskets and on the trays. Thousands of gaping mouths silently screamed at him. He walked away from the quayside, and climbed up a hill. Here it was quiet. The life of the day had hardly begun yet. He looked up at the window of a small house and wished that a woman would open it and beckon him upstairs. But all windows remained shut.

Slowly he walked back to the hotel. Paul was not in the room. A letter was lying on the dressing table. Paul had written:

'It is not within the realms of possibility that our relationship could ever change. The fact that we are in some matters fundamentally different, will always trigger off controversies, but this should not be the cause of such aggressive quarrels in the future. At present they spring from the excessive stress we're both under. (By the way, I am aware that I misunderstood you last night.) All this should be self-evident to you, as it is to me. I am astonished how such thoughts as you express them in your note, could have gained a footing?'

Later the brothers took a stroll through the town and, standing in front of Grieg's statue in a little quadrangle, Paul said:

"How many great people this little country has produced! There is Grieg, the composer, Munch, the painter, Hamsun, the writer and, of course, the great Ibsen."

"I've been to the 'Doll's House' – in Brünn. I didn't really

279

understand it," said Martin.

"There are not many dramatists who could have written a play about the relationships within our family," said Paul.

"You mean, Ibsen could have done so?"

"Perhaps it would have been too difficult a task, even for him."

The brothers moved on, arm in arm, laughing.

The boat left Bergen on the 21st March. It was a small boat in a large convoy. It took six days to cross the North Sea. The boat was a freighter and the heavy seas tossed it about like a toy. By the second day all the passengers had crept into their bunks in the belly of the boat and made themselves invisible. Paul and Martin had a large cabin to themselves and lived mainly on oranges. Paul was very sick and Martin suffered from giddiness. After a day or two, Martin had got used to the pitching and tossing and he could have gone up on deck, but chose not to leave Paul. They both were constantly aware of the danger of German Submarines and neither of them could believe they would one day land in Britain. Men and the heavens seemed to be in league against them, there was no way of escape from either of them.

But on the last day they both stood on deck, ruffled by the wind, and saw the large cranes. Newcastle. Then the landing formalities. A smiling man from the Refugee Committee was waiting and led the group to the station platform. They were told that relatives had been informed of their arrival and would welcome them at Kings Cross Station. The brothers tried to picture the welcome but could not. As it happened, neither their father nor their mother was waiting for them. The man from the Committee, after handing over all the others to their excited relatives, expressed regret. Obviously something had gone wrong. He assured the brothers that he would make some arrangement for the night. The brothers were to remain here, seated on the bench under the large clock. Neither Paul nor Martin were particularly disappointed at not seeing the parents. Their feelings were dulled.

They sat together, close, so that their heads nearly touched.

The station was blacked out, but there was enough light to show its ugliness. The smell of engines, damp and biting, sharp whistles and the sounds of hurrying people. It was cold. Martin thought that it was a good thing they each had their own overcoat. They sat for a long time and felt sleepy. Martin's head had fallen on Paul's shoulder. They were woken by someone shouting out their name.

"Rosen. Rosen."

Paul shook Martin and they followed the taxi driver as they had followed guards and soldiers so many times before. The taxi stopped outside a boarding-house in Bloomsbury.

They were shown to their room, only big enough to hold one bed. The proprietor apologised. He had had no warning. There was no double room vacant. Paul, whose English was quite good, said that it did not matter. They had slept in worse conditions in the past. When Martin got up next morning to find the bathroom, the unknown smell of fried bacon greeted him.

They had their breakfast by themselves, all the other guests had already left. Paul picked up a newspaper from a table which had not yet been cleared.

"Refugees unwelcome," he translated for Martin who spoke little English, "it is the intention of the Government to return refugees to their country of origin, once the war is over."

"Well," said Martin, "we have nowhere to go back to."

"But it shows that Great Britain is not particularly friendly to refugees," said Paul.

"Still, they got us here," said Martin.

Later, a young woman collected them.

"Have you had a good journey? Are you happy to be here now? Did you have a good breakfast? English breakfasts are famous, you know."

She did not expect any answers.

"We shall go to the Refugee Centre," she said, "it is only a few minutes walk from here, in Woburn Square."

While she kept on chatting, Martin counted the number of Refugee Centres he had been to, there was the one in Brünn, one in Kattowitz, one in Wilna and now here in London.

Martin wanted to ask the young woman whether they had had snow in London, but he realised that this was not very important.

When they entered the building, Martin saw his father, the back of his father, and he called out: "We are here. Here."

But there were so many people milling around, everybody seemed to be in a hurry and there was so much noise. The young woman pushed the brothers forward up the stairs.

"Father is here," Martin said, "he's downstairs."

"You must be mistaken," Paul replied, "the parents probably don't even know yet, that we have arrived in this country."

But when they came downstairs after signing various papers, they saw their father and they embraced him. They thought that he had aged since they had seen him last. Then father rang their mother.

"They are here, Sarah — child. They are standing next to me."

Paul and Martin listened in turn to their mother's uncontrolled sobbing.

Over lunch, father told them that mother was not on her own in Richmond. Frau Perlmutter was with her. "You remember Frau Perlmutter? She has been a good friend of ours for a very long time."

Martin remembered. When he was little he had overheard that Frau Perlmutter was suffering from depressions. This had frightened him.

"She also has got a tale to tell," said father. "Did you know that her son lives in Australia? She and her second husband were on their way to join him. The ship was torpedoed and she saw her husband die in the sea. Apparently he could not hold on to a piece of debris for long. No doubt you will hear about it from her."

'I don't want to hear,' thought Martin, 'I don't want to hear anything. I don't want to listen to Frau Perlmutter. I don't want to meet her. I just want to be with the parents and with Paul.'

Mother was waiting for them and Frau Perlmutter stood behind her. They were both crying.

"You are safe," cried mother, "you are safe. That is all

282

that matters. Don't tell me what you have gone through. I don't want to know. I don't ever want to know. You are safe. You are here. You are both very thin. There's plenty to eat here, plenty of everything."

Mother: "Your father was marvellous when we thought we had lost you. He kept me going. I don't know what I would have done without him. I was quite ready to kill myself. But he convinced me that we would see you again. He prevented me from putting my head into the gas oven. And, of course, our landlady assured us that, when she was in a trance, she had seen you walking towards us. But you know, you must know, that lately your father has been behaving as he has always behaved. Frau Perlmutter, I'm certain he has started something with her. You will have noticed they are very close . . ."

Paul: "But mother . . ."

Mother: "I always say what I think. It is best to call a spade a spade."

Paul: "You are not serious, mother, when you suggest that . . ."

Mother: "Your father has an affair with her? Of course, I am serious.

Paul: "But that's nonsense, and you know it."

Mother: "You don't know your father as well as I do, Paul. But the main thing is that I have got you . . . both of you."

Father: "It was not easy living with your mother. I had to think how best to occupy her. We went blackberrying a lot last summer. We wrote to you about it. The landlady has been a help. She told mother several times that she had seen you. Are you both all right? Is there anything you need? You are without watches. Woolworth sells cheap ones. We shall go to Kingston next week and buy them. Have you written the diary yet? Don't show it to mother. She doesn't want to know about your experiences. By the way, mother thinks there's something going on between Frau Perlmutter and myself. Rubbish, of course. Utter nonsense. I'm not in the least interested in her. What a relief you're both here. Have a good rest and then we shall see. Martin, can you still type? Our landlady has got a typewriter. There's a letter I should like you to type for me. I've got an idea which has got possibilities for development."

The brothers shared a large double bed. They quarrelled a lot.

One afternoon in April, Martin walked down to the river. He squatted near the river's edge. The water of the Thames looked angry.

'Like me,' he thought, 'I am also angry. Nothing has changed. Everything is as it always has been.'

Paul tapped him on the shoulder.

"We were looking for you," Paul said, "we wondered where you were. You really should try to make more of an effort to fall in with the parents' wishes. You're so concerned with yourself that you have no time left for anyone else."

"We shan't be together for very long," said Martin. He did not know what made him say so.

It takes a long time to arrive anywhere.
There would still be many departures.

*   *   *   *

A few weeks later, in May, the brothers were interned as 'enemy aliens' and later shipped to Canada. Paul was released from internment in December the following year and returned to England. Martin had to stay behind in Canada until July 1942. He was then transferred to an internment camp on the Isle of Man and released in the autumn.